MATH TRAILBLAZERS™

Grade 4

Unit Resource Guide
Unit 13
Division

SECOND EDITION

A Mathematical Journey Using Science and Language Arts

KENDALL/HUNT PUBLISHING COMPANY
4050 Westmark Drive   Dubuque, Iowa 52002

A TIMS® Curriculum
University of Illinois at Chicago

UIC The University of Illinois at Chicago

The original edition was based on work supported by the National Science Foundation under grant No. MDR 9050226 and the University of Illinois at Chicago. Any opinions, findings, and conclusions or recommendations expressed in this publication are those of the author(s) and do not necessarily reflect the views of the granting agencies.

LETTER HOME

Division

Date: _____

Dear Family Member:

To begin this unit, the class will conduct a survey on the amount of television a fourth-grader watches. In analyzing the survey data, your child will need to solve division problems. *Math Trailblazers™* emphasizes that there are many correct methods that can be used to perform division.

Your child will begin work with division by interpreting and writing division stories. He or she will use base-ten pieces to model division problems and then learn a paper-and-pencil method. This method is similar to the traditional method. While encouraging students to make good estimates of "how many times does this number go into that number," the method will still work with estimates that are too low. Research shows that students who were taught this method were better able to

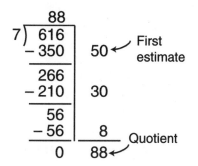

A paper-and-pencil method

explain the meaning of the steps than those who were taught the traditional method. In everyday life and work, we often need quick mental estimates for the solutions to division problems. Students who use this method become better at estimating quotients. When we help students understand the mathematics they do, we communicate to them the idea that mathematics makes sense.

You can help your child by doing the following at home:

• Ask your child to show you how he or she is learning division.

• More information on the TV Survey will be sent home. Help your child keep track of the amount of television he or she watches.

• Your child will practice the division facts for the last group of facts called the "last six facts." These are the division facts related to the following six multiplication facts: $4 \times 6, 4 \times 7,$ $4 \times 8, 6 \times 7, 6 \times 8,$ and 7×8. So, students will practice $24 \div 4, 24 \div 6, 28 \div 7,$ and so on. Help your child gain fluency with these facts by using the *Triangle Flash Cards*.

Please contact me if you have any questions or concerns.

Sincerely,

_____

UNIT OUTLINE

Division

Pacing Suggestions

- Use the recommended number of sessions for each lesson as a guide. Students develop their division skills in this unit, but it is not necessary to stop until all students master each concept and skill. Distributed practice of small sets of division problems and sets of word problems are included in each of the succeeding units in the lessons, Daily Practice and Problems, and Home Practice.

- Lesson 5 *Plant Growth* begins a laboratory investigation that shows the growth patterns in plants. In this lesson students identify the variables in the experiment, draw pictures, set up data tables, and plant seeds. Students collect data on the height of their plants for approximately 21 days. Unit 15 Lesson 1 *Plant Growth Conclusion* begins the study of patterns in that unit. Students analyze their plant growth data by identifying patterns in their data tables and graphs. Note that there are less than 21 days between these two lessons according to the suggested number of sessions in the unit outlines for Units 14 and 15. You may need to teach this lesson later in Unit 15. Setting up the laboratory investigation and planting seeds are appropriate activities for science as well as math.

Components Key: SG = Student Guide, DAB = Discovery Assignment Book, AB = Adventure Book, URG = Unit Resource Guide, and DPP = Daily Practice and Problems

	Sessions	Description	Supplies
LESSON 1			
TV Survey SG pages 358–363 DAB pages 219–221 URG pages 26–42 DPP A–F	3	**ACTIVITY:** In an introductory session, students plan the *TV Survey.* Then, students collect data about the amount of TV they watch in a four-day period while continuing with the other lessons in this unit. After the four-day period, students organize, graph, and analyze the data.	• calculators • envelopes
LESSON 2			
Division SG pages 364–370 URG pages 43–54 DPP G–L	3	**ACTIVITY:** Students are introduced to long division by modeling with the base-ten pieces. The symbols for division are discussed, and the "forgiving method" for long division is introduced.	• base-ten pieces
LESSON 3			
More Division SG pages 371–373 DAB page 223 URG pages 55–65 DPP M–R	3–4	**ACTIVITY:** Students represent division problems with base-ten pieces and use the forgiving method. This lesson emphasizes three- and four-digit dividends. Using estimation to make good predictions is stressed.	• base-ten pieces

	Sessions	Description	Supplies
LESSON 4 **Solving Problems Using Multiplication and Division** SG pages 374–378 URG pages 66–74 DPP S–V	2	**ACTIVITY:** Students solve a variety of word problems involving multiplication and division. A quiz is included in this lesson. **ASSESSMENT PAGE:** *Unit 13 Quiz,* Unit Resource Guide, page 72.	• calculators
LESSON 5 **Plant Growth** SG pages 379–381 URG pages 75–84 DPP W–Z	2	**LAB:** Students begin a lab that investigates the growth pattern of plants. They identify the manipulated, responding, and fixed variables for this experiment. Students plant seeds, choose one plant to follow, and take measurements of the plant's growth over time. Students will graph and analyze their data in Lesson 1 of Unit 15.	• container for planting seeds • seeds • graduated cylinders • rulers • potting soil • paper towels • centimeter rulers

CONNECTIONS

A current list of connections is available at www.mathtrailblazers.com.

Literature

Suggested Title

■ Burnie, David. *Eyewitness Books: Plants.* D. K. Publishing, New York, 2000.

Software

■ *Graph Master* allows students to collect data and create their own graphs.

■ *Kid Pix* allows students to create their own illustrations.

■ *Math Munchers Deluxe* provides practice in basic facts in an arcade-like game.

■ *Math Mysteries: Advanced Whole Numbers* is a series of structured multistep word problems dealing with whole numbers.

■ *Math Workshop Deluxe* develops math fact proficiency.

■ *Mighty Math Calculating Crew* poses short answer questions about number operations and money.

■ *Mighty Math Number Heroes* poses short answer questions about number operations.

■ *Number Sense—Divide & Conquer* develops conceptual understanding of the division process.

Division

> "Procedural fluency and conceptual understanding are often seen as competing for attention in school mathematics. But pitting skill against understanding creates a false dichotomy. . . . the two are interwoven. Understanding makes learning skills easier, less susceptible to common errors, and less prone to forgetting. By the same token, a certain level of skill is required to learn many mathematical concepts with understanding, and using procedures can help strengthen and develop that understanding."
>
> From the National Research Council "The Strands of Mathematical Proficiency" in *Adding It Up: Helping Children Learn Mathematics,* 2001.

This unit focuses on developing children's conceptual understanding of division and introduces a paper-and-pencil method for computing. The concepts of division that children have developed in the first three grades is expanded here. Division is reviewed first in the form of stories. Students need a firm conceptual basis in order to perform computations with symbols (Hiebert, 1989, 1999; National Research Council, 2001). Thus, students model division with base-ten pieces before tackling long division.

Paper-and-pencil methods are introduced in the *Student Guide* in the context of the *equal sharing* or *partitive division* model, with children sharing a box of marbles.

If two students share 75 marbles, how many marbles will each student receive? 75 ÷ 2 = 37 marbles with 1 remaining.

Problems in the *Student Guide* also include the *equal grouping* or *measurement division* model.

75 marbles are divided evenly and stored in bags. If each bag holds 5 marbles, how many bags are needed? 75 ÷ 5 = 15 bags

The different types of division models are discussed in the Background section of Unit 4.

Given the vast amount of time and the frustration involved in learning the long division algorithm traditionally taught in the United States, we instead use what we call the "forgiving method." Sometimes it is referred to as the "subtraction method." While this method may seem new, written record of it appears in a book published in 1729 while the first record of the traditional method appears in a publication dating from 1491 (Hazekamp, 1978). As with the traditional method, the forgiving method requires students to estimate quotients. The forgiving method is different in two ways. First, the student starts by estimating the entire quotient instead of the first digit. Secondly, if the estimate is too small, the student can continue with the procedure. This greatly alleviates the frustration of having to erase, and to some extent, allows one to get around a forgotten multiplication fact. An example of how the method works follows.

In a problem such as 6343 ÷ 7, we guess how many times 7 goes into 6343. An advantage to this method is that it encourages students to make good estimates. At the beginning, however, children have a difficult time doing this. If this is the case, encourage them to take a guess. Also encourage guesses that are "nice" numbers, such as tens, hundreds, and thousands. As long as the guess is not too large, it can be used. We record the guesses in a column to the right of the problem.

A typical student response follows:

Student: I'll guess 100.

$$
\begin{array}{r|l}
7\,\overline{)\,6343} & \\
-\,700 & 100 \\
\hline
5643 &
\end{array}
$$

It is instructive for children to see that this first estimate is way too low—much of the 6343 still remains. The teacher can take the opportunity to suggest 1000, which children should recognize as too large.

Student: Since 100 was way too small and 1000 is too big, I'll try 500:

$$
\begin{array}{r|l}
7\,\overline{)\,6343} & \\
-\,700 & 100 \\
\hline
5643 & \\
-\,3500 & 500 \\
\hline
2143 &
\end{array}
$$

Notice that we use a vertical line to help keep the estimates lined up properly.

Student: 500 won't work again since $7 \times 500 = 3500$ and I only have 2143 left. I'll try 300:

$$
\begin{array}{r|l}
7\,\overline{)\,6343} & \\
-\,700 & 100 \\
\hline
5643 & \\
-\,3500 & 500 \\
\hline
2143 & \\
-\,2100 & 300 \\
\hline
43 &
\end{array}
$$

Student: Now I have 43 left. I know $7 \times 6 = 42$, so I'll try 6:

$$
\begin{array}{r|l}
& 906\text{R}1 \\
7\,\overline{)\,6343} & \\
-\,700 & 100 \\
\hline
5643 & \\
-\,3500 & 500 \\
\hline
2143 & \\
-\,2100 & 300 \\
\hline
43 & \\
-\,42 & 6 \\
\hline
1 &
\end{array}
$$

Student: The number of 7s that go into 6343 is $100 + 500 + 300 + 6 = 906$. The remainder is 1.

Another advantage to this method is that it cuts down on the amount of regrouping that needs to be done since many of the subtractions involve numbers with ending zeros. This helps reduce the number of errors. Also, children practice multiplying numbers that end in zero and practice estimating quotients. When the "best" estimate is used consistently, the method is actually the same as the traditional algorithm, except the estimates are written in a column to the right of the problem, rather than across the top (National Research Council, 2001).

Research has shown that low-ability students show better retention and understanding when taught division with this method and become better estimators of quotients. Students who were taught the forgiving method were better at solving unfamiliar problems and were better able to explain the meaning of the steps (van Engen and Gibb, 1956). Another study found that students who were taught both the forgiving and traditional methods did not confuse the methods and that the total amount of time needed to learn both was the same as the amount of time needed to learn one of the methods (Scott, 1963). Understanding rote procedures enables students to perform mathematical tasks with confidence and meaning. When children understand the mathematics they do, they come to believe that mathematics makes sense, and they are better able to think and reason flexibly.

> **Content Note**
>
> **Method vs. Algorithm.** Since the forgiving method allows us many ways of proceeding, we call this a method and not an algorithm. An algorithm would mimic a computer program and do the same steps each time.

Resources

- Hazekamp, Donald W. "Teaching Multiplication and Division Algorithms." In *Developing Computational Skills: 1978 Yearbook,* Marilyn N. Suydam and Robert E. Reys (eds). National Council of Teachers of Mathematics, Reston, VA, 1978.
- Hiebert, J. "Relationships between Research and the NCTM *Standards*." *Journal for Research in Mathematics Education,* 30(1), pp. 3–19, 1999.
- Hiebert, James. "The Struggle to Link Written Symbols with Understandings: An Update." *Arithmetic Teacher,* 36 (7), 38–44, 1989.
- National Research Council. "The Strands of Mathematical Proficiency" and "Developing Proficiency with Whole Numbers." In *Adding It Up: Helping Children Learn Mathematics.* J. Kilpatrick, J. Swafford, and B. Findell, eds. National Academy Press, Washington, DC, 2001.
- *Principles and Standards for School Mathematics.* National Council of Teachers of Mathematics, Reston, VA, 2000.
- Scott, Lloyd. "A Study of Teaching Division through the Use of Two Algorithms." *School Science and Mathematics,* pp. 739–752, December, 1963.
- van Engen, Henry, and Glenadine E. Gibb. *General Mental Functions Associated with Division,* Iowa State Teachers College, Cedar Falls, Iowa, 1956.

Assessment Indicators

- Can students collect, organize, graph, and analyze data?
- Can students represent division using base-ten pieces?
- Can students divide with 1-digit divisors using paper and pencil?
- Can students interpret remainders?
- Can students estimate quotients?
- Can students solve problems involving multiplication and division?
- Do students demonstrate fluency with the 12 division facts related to the last six facts
  ($24 \div 4$, $24 \div 6$, $28 \div 4$, $28 \div 7$, $32 \div 4$, $32 \div 8$, $42 \div 6$, $42 \div 7$, $48 \div 6$, $48 \div 8$, $56 \div 7$, $56 \div 8$)?

OBSERVATIONAL ASSESSMENT RECORD

A1 Can students collect, organize, graph, and analyze data?

A2 Can students represent division using base-ten pieces?

A3 Can students divide with 1-digit divisors using paper and pencil?

A4 Can students interpret remainders?

A5 Can students estimate quotients?

A6 Can students solve problems involving multiplication and division?

A7 Do students demonstrate fluency with the 12 division facts related to the last six facts (24 ÷ 4, 24 ÷ 6, 28 ÷ 4, 28 ÷ 7, 32 ÷ 4, 32 ÷ 8, 42 ÷ 6, 42 ÷ 7, 48 ÷ 6, 48 ÷ 8, 56 ÷ 7, 56 ÷ 8)?

A8 _____

Name	A1	A2	A3	A4	A5	A6	A7	A8	Comments
1.									
2.									
3.									
4.									
5.									
6.									
7.									
8.									
9.									
10.									
11.									
12.									
13.									

Name	A1	A2	A3	A4	A5	A6	A7	A8	Comments
14.									
15.									
16.									
17.									
18.									
19.									
20.									
21.									
22.									
23.									
24.									
25.									
26.									
27.									
28.									
29.									
30.									
31.									
32.									

Daily Practice and Problems

Division

Two Daily Practice and Problems (DPP) items are included for each class session listed in the Unit Outline. The first item is always a Bit and the second is either a Task or a Challenge. Refer to the Daily Practice and Problems and Home Practice Guide in the *Teacher Implementation Guide* for further information. A Scope and Sequence Chart for the DPP can be found in the Scope and Sequence Chart & the NCTM *Principles and Standards* section of the *Teacher Implementation Guide.*

A DPP Menu for Unit 13

Eight icons designate the subject matter of the DPP items. Each item falls into one or more of the categories listed below. A brief menu of the DPP items in Unit 13 follows.

N Number Sense A, E–J, L, U–W, Y	**Computation** A, F, H–J, M, N, P, R, T, V	**Time** E, F, M	**Geometry**
Math Facts B–D, H, K, Q, S, U	**$ Money** T, X	**Measurement**	**Data** I, O, Z

Practice and Assessment of the Multiplication Facts

The DPP for this unit continues the systematic strategies-based approach to learning the division facts. This unit provides practice and assessment of the related division facts for the last six facts (4 × 6, 4 × 7, 4 × 8, 6 × 7, 6 × 8, and 7 × 8). Students practice 24 ÷ 6, 24 ÷ 4, 28 ÷ 4, and so on. At this point in the year, students concentrate on using efficient strategies in order to gain fluency with these facts. The *Triangle Flash Cards* for this group are located after the Home Practice in the *Discovery Assignment Book* and in the *Unit Resource Guide,* Generic Section. A discussion of the flash cards and how to use them can be found in item B of the DPP. A quiz on these facts is provided in item S.

For more information about the distribution and assessment of the math facts, see the TIMS Tutor: *Math Facts* in the *Teacher Implementation Guide.* Also refer to the Daily Practice and Problems Guides in the *Unit Resource Guides* for Units 3 and 9.

Daily Practice and Problems

Students may solve the items individually, in groups, or as a class. The items may also be assigned for homework.

Student Questions	Teacher Notes

A **Multiplication Practice**

Solve the following using a paper-and-pencil method or mental math. Estimate to make sure your answers are reasonable.

1. A. $46 \times 3 =$

   B. $76 \times 80 =$

   C. $92 \times 47 =$

   D. $25 \times 30 =$

2. Explain your estimation strategy for Question 1C.

TIMS Bit

1. A. 138

   B. 6080

   C. 4324

   D. 750

2. Possible strategy:

   $90 \times 50 = 4500$

The Last Six Facts

With a partner, use your *Triangle Flash Cards: Last Six Facts* to quiz each other on the related division facts for the last six multiplication facts (24 ÷ 6, 24 ÷ 4, 28 ÷ 7, 28 ÷ 4, 32 ÷ 8, 32 ÷ 4, 42 ÷ 7, 42 ÷ 6, 48 ÷ 8, 48 ÷ 6, 56 ÷ 8, 56 ÷ 7). Ask your partner first to cover the numbers in the squares. Use the two uncovered numbers to solve a division fact. Then, ask your partner to cover the numbers in the circles. Use the uncovered numbers to solve a division fact.

After each time through the cards, separate them into three piles: those facts you know and can answer quickly, those that you can figure out with a strategy, and those that you need to learn. Practice the last two piles again and then make a list of the facts you need to practice at home for homework.

Circle the facts you know and can answer quickly on your *Division Facts I Know* chart.

TIMS Task

The flash cards for the last six facts can be found after the Home Practice in the *Discovery Assignment Book* and in the *Unit Resource Guide* Generic Section. Discuss strategies students use to find the answers to the facts, emphasizing those strategies that are more efficient than others.

In Part 1 of the Home Practice, students are reminded to bring home their *Triangle Flash Cards: Last Six Facts.*

Inform students when the quiz on the last six facts will be. This quiz appears in item S.

Multiplication Facts Review

A. $8 \times 4 =$ B. $7 \times 4 =$

C. $6 \times 7 =$ D. $7 \times 8 =$

E. $6 \times 8 =$ F. $4 \times 6 =$

TIMS Bit

Discuss strategies students use to solve the facts, emphasizing those strategies that are more efficient than others. Students might use a fact they know to solve another. For example, to solve 6×7, students might first think 5×7 is 35. Then, adding on one more 7 to 35 will give 42. Students who know the square numbers well might use the square numbers to solve "close" facts. For example, to solve 7×8, first think "7×7 is 49." Then, add 7 to 49 to get 56. Students may also say, "I just know it." Recall is obviously an efficient strategy.

 Fact Families for $\times$ and $\div$

The following four facts belong to the same fact family.

$4 \times 6 = 24$ $6 \times 4 = 24$

$24 \div 6 = 4$ $24 \div 4 = 6$

Solve each fact. Then, name three other facts that are in the same fact family.

A. $28 \div 7 =$

B. $7 \times 8 =$

C. $7 \times 6 =$

D. $32 \div 4 =$

E. $8 \times 6 =$

TIMS Task

Complete this item orally as a class. One student can solve the given fact and other students can name each of the other related facts.

A. 4; $28 \div 4 = 7$
   $7 \times 4 = 28$
   $4 \times 7 = 28$

B. 56; $8 \times 7 = 56$
   $56 \div 8 = 7$
   $56 \div 7 = 8$

C. 42; $6 \times 7 = 42$
   $42 \div 7 = 6$
   $42 \div 6 = 7$

D. 8; $32 \div 8 = 4$
   $8 \times 4 = 32$
   $4 \times 8 = 32$

E. 48; $6 \times 8 = 48$
   $48 \div 6 = 8$
   $48 \div 8 = 6$

Trumpet Practice

Ana's trumpet teacher told her to practice $\frac{3}{4}$ hour every day. Since 1 hour = 60 minutes, Ana used this number sentence to find the number of minutes she must practice each day: $\frac{3}{4} = \frac{?}{60}$.

1. Complete Ana's number sentence to find the number of minutes in $\frac{3}{4}$ hour.

2. Use Ana's method or your own strategies to find the following:

   A. How many minutes are in $\frac{1}{4}$ hour?

   B. How many minutes are in $\frac{1}{2}$ hour?

   C. How many minutes are in $\frac{1}{3}$ hour?

   D. How many minutes are in $\frac{1}{6}$ hour?

   E. How many minutes are in $1\frac{1}{4}$ hours?

   F. How many minutes are in 3.5 hours?

TIMS Bit

Discuss students' strategies for solving the problems. If students have trouble developing a strategy, encourage them to use equivalent fractions as in Unit 12 Lesson 5. This item will help students as they analyze the data for *TV Survey* in Lesson 1 of this unit.

1. 45 minutes

2. A. 15 minutes

   B. 30 minutes

   C. 20 minutes

   D. 10 minutes

   E. 75 minutes

   F. 210 minutes

TV Survey Data

1. Last night, Shannon watched 3 hours of TV. How many minutes is 3 hours?

2. Maya watched 2.5 hours of TV. How many minutes is this?

3. Nicholas watched $2\frac{1}{4}$ hours of TV. How many minutes is this?

4. How many minutes did these three students watch in all? How many hours?

TIMS Task

Discuss students' strategies for Question 4. Students can convert the total number of minutes to hours by dividing by 60. They will need to be able to correctly interpret the remainder. They may also solve the addition problem: $3 + 2.5 + 2\frac{1}{4}$. Students should remember from Units 10 and 12 that $2.5 = 2\frac{1}{2}$ and $\frac{1}{2} + \frac{1}{4} = \frac{3}{4}$. So, $3 + 2.5 + 2\frac{1}{4} = 7\frac{3}{4}$. Students get more practice converting minutes to hours when they resume Lesson 1, after the *TV Survey* data collection is complete. See Lesson Guide 1.

1. 180 minutes

2. 150 minutes

3. 135 minutes

4. 465 minutes; 7 hours and 45 minutes or 7.75 hours

 Skip Counting by 6 and 60

1. Skip count by 6s from 6 to 60. Start this way: 6, 12, 18, . . .

2. Skip count by 60s from 60 to 600. Start this way: 60, 120, 180, . . .

TIMS Bit

Students may use a calculator to help them skip count. This item will help students as they analyze their data for *TV Survey.*

Student Questions	Teacher Notes

 Multiples of 10 and 100

Solve each pair of related number sentences.

A. $4 \times 80 =$ and $320 \div 4 =$

B. $40 \times 6 =$ and $240 \div 40 =$

C. $70 \times 4 =$ and $280 \div 70 =$

D. $60 \times 7 =$ and $420 \div 7 =$

E. $8 \times 70 =$ and $560 \div 70 =$

F. $80 \times 60 =$ and $4800 \div 80 =$

TIMS Task

A. 320; 80

B. 240; 6

C. 280; 4

D. 420; 60

E. 560; 8

F. 4800; 60

More TV Survey Data

Linda watched 45 minutes of TV on Monday, 135 minutes on Tuesday, and 30 minutes on Wednesday. She did not watch TV on Thursday.

1. Use a calculator to find the mean number of minutes of TV Linda watched each day.

2. Give a quick estimate for the median number of minutes watched.

TIMS Bit

1. $(45 + 135 + 30 + 0) \div 4 = 52.5$ minutes

2. 0, 30, 45, 135; The actual median is 37.5, the number midway between 30 and 45. Numbers between 35 and 40 are good estimates.

Moving Out

Use base-ten pieces or shorthand to solve the following. Explain any remainders.

1. Ming is helping his mother pack the books on the living room bookshelves. There are 46 books to pack and 4 boxes. How many books can Ming pack in each box?

2. Ming's mother hired a moving company. A father and two sons evenly split their pay of $225. How much did each person earn?

TIMS Task

In Lesson 2, students solve division problems with base-ten pieces and write division stories. In Lesson 3, students learn a paper-and-pencil method for dividing.

1. $46 \div 4 = 11$ R2; two boxes can be filled with 11 books and two boxes can be filled with 12 books. Using base-ten shorthand, the total number of books is shown as:

/\// :····

Box 1   Box 2

/ · |·

Box 3   Box 4

|·· |··

2. $225 \div 3 = \$75$
Exchange 2 flats for 20 skinnies, for a total of 22 skinnies. Divide the 22 skinnies into 3 groups of 7 skinnies. Exchange the one leftover skinny for 10 bits, for a total of 15 bits.

□□ // ·····

Father | Son 1
/\/|| | /\\//
// ·····| \| ·····

Son 2
//\//
/\ ·····

Student Questions	Teacher Notes

 Related Division Facts

TIMS Bit

Solve each fact. Then, name the other division fact in the same fact family.

A. $56 \div 8 =$

B. $32 \div 4 =$

C. $42 \div 7 =$

D. $24 \div 4 =$

E. $48 \div 6 =$

F. $28 \div 7 =$

A. 7; $56 \div 7 = 8$

B. 8; $32 \div 8 = 4$

C. 6; $42 \div 6 = 7$

D. 6; $24 \div 6 = 4$

E. 8; $48 \div 8 = 6$

F. 4; $28 \div 4 = 7$

 Draw One Whole

TIMS Task

You will need some pattern blocks to complete this item.

1. If the shape below is one whole, draw $\frac{1}{4}$.

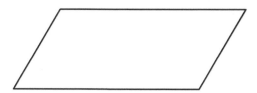

2. Draw $1\frac{1}{2}$.

1. The whole can be formed from 4 green triangles. Therefore, 1 green triangle is $\frac{1}{4}$.

2. Figures may vary. Two possibilities are shown below. Part of the figure should contain the shape in Question 1 (1 whole). $\frac{1}{2}$ of the figure is the same as two green triangles or one blue rhombus.

Student Questions	Teacher Notes

 **TV Survey**

Use paper and pencil or mental math to solve the following problems.

1. According to a recent study, the average American eighth-grader spends about 4 hours a day watching TV. How many hours in a year will an eighth-grader spend watching TV?

2. A school year is approximately 180 days long. How many hours is a student in school, if a school day is 6 hours long?

TIMS Bit

1. 1460 hours

2. 1080 hours

Building with Cubes

1. Roberto made a building out of 168 connecting cubes. Each floor contains 6 cubes. How many floors are in the building?

2. Shannon has 126 cubes. The building she creates has 9 floors. Each floor has the same number of cubes.
   How many cubes are in each floor of Shannon's building?

3. Nila has $\frac{1}{2}$ of the number of cubes as Roberto. Nila's building has 7 floors. If each floor has the same number of cubes, how many cubes are in each floor of Nila's building?

TIMS Task

1. 28 floors;
   $168 \div 6 = 28$ floors

2. 14 cubes;
   $126 \div 9 = 14$ cubes

3. 12 cubes; Nila has 84 cubes. $84 \div 7 = 12$

Student Questions	Teacher Notes

 TV Survey Graph

1. How many students watched between 2 and 3 hours of TV?

2. How many students are included in this data?

3. How many students watched 4 hours or more?

4. How many watched less than 2 hours?

5. What is the most common number of hours watched?

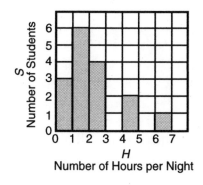

Number of Hours per Night

 TIMS Bit

1. 4 students

2. 16 students

3. 3 students

4. 9 students

5. between 1 and 2 hours of TV

 Writing Division Stories

Write a story for 256 ÷ 7. Remember to talk about the remainder. Then, find the answer. You may use base-ten shorthand or another paper-and-pencil method to solve the problem.

 TIMS Task

Encourage students to share their stories. For example, 256 cantaloupes are being shipped to the grocery store.

7 cantaloupes fit in each crate. How many crates are needed? 256 ÷ 7 = 36 R4; 37 crates would be needed.

Student Questions	Teacher Notes

Q Division Practice

A. $60 \div 8 =$

B. $25 \div 4 =$

C. $35 \div 8 =$

D. $50 \div 6 =$

E. $30 \div 7 =$

F. $45 \div 6 =$

TIMS Bit

A. 7 R4

B. 6 R1

C. 4 R3

D. 8 R2

E. 4 R2

F. 7 R3

R Paper-and-Pencil Division

Describe how you can decide which of the problems below will have a remainder and which will come out even. Then, solve the problems using paper and pencil. Check your answers using multiplication.

1. $87 \div 3$

2. $178 \div 2$

3. $577 \div 6$

TIMS Task

87 is divisible by 3.
8 + 7 = 15; 15 is a multiple of 3.
178 is divisible by 2 since it is an even number. 577 is not evenly divisible by 6. 577 is not even.

Students may use the forgiving method of division which is taught in Lesson 3 to solve these problems.

1. 29   2. 89   3. 96 R1

Below is a sample solution strategy for 577 ÷ 6 using the forgiving method.

```
        96R1
  6 )577
   - 300 |  50
     277
   - 180 |  30
      97
   -  60 |  10
      37
   -  36 |   6
       1    96R1
```

Student Questions	Teacher Notes

 Facts Quiz: Last Six Facts

A. $24 \div 6 =$ B. $28 \div 7 =$

C. $56 \div 7 =$ D. $32 \div 8 =$

E. $48 \div 8 =$ F. $24 \div 4 =$

G. $42 \div 6 =$ H. $32 \div 4 =$

I. $48 \div 6 =$ J. $56 \div 8 =$

K. $28 \div 4 =$ L. $42 \div 7 =$

TIMS Bit

This quiz is on the last six facts. We recommend 2 minutes for this quiz. You might want to allow students to change pens after the time is up and complete the remaining problems in a different color.

After students take the test, have them update their *Division Facts I Know* charts.

 Saving Quarters

1. The Anderson family saves quarters in a jar. They divide the quarters they save among their four children. If they save 345 quarters, how many quarters does each child receive?

2. How much money does each child receive?

TIMS Task

In Lesson 3, students learn a paper-and-pencil method for division—the forgiving method. Encourage them to use this method to solve Question 1.

1. 86 quarters; 1 quarter left over

2. 86 quarters × 25¢ = 2150¢ or $21.50.

Note: If the 1 quarter in the remainder is traded for 25 pennies, each child can receive an additional 6¢ (25¢ ÷ 4 = 6¢ R1¢) with 1 penny left over.

Zero and Division

Solve the following. Justify your reasoning using a related multiplication sentence.

A. $7 \div 0 =$ B. $0 \div 0 =$

C. $0 \div 7 =$ D. $7 \div 1 =$

TIMS Bit

A. $7 \div 0$ is undefined since there is no number that makes $0 \times ? = 7$ a true statement.

B. $0 \div 0$ is undefined since there is no one number that makes $0 \times ? = 0$ true.

C. $0 \div 7 = 0$ since $0 \times 7 = 0$.

D. $7 \div 1 = 7$ since $1 \times 7 = 7$.

Even Teams

Nicholas took his cousin Stan to his Wilderness Club picnic. On the way home, Stan and Nicholas wondered how many kids came to the picnic. Nicholas said, "Well, the leaders divided us evenly into 2 groups for the scavenger hunt. For the other games, they divided us evenly into 3 groups, 5 groups, and 6 groups. Finally, when we had the relay races, they divided us evenly into 7 groups." What is the fewest possible number of kids that came to the picnic?

TIMS Challenge

Students can use their divisibility rules and what they have learned about factors and multiples to solve this problem. Encourage students to use calculators to find the smallest number that is divisible by 2, 3, 5, 6, and 7:
$5 \times 6 \times 7 = 210$ kids.

Students can also skip count by 7s, until they find a number that is also divisible by 2, 3, 5, and 6.

What Fraction?

1. $\frac{2}{3}$ of Mrs. Dewey's class went on a field trip.

   A. What fraction of the class did not go on the field trip?

   B. Did more or less than $\frac{1}{2}$ of the class go on the trip?

2. $\frac{3}{8}$ of Mrs. Randall's class went on the field trip.

   A. What fraction of the class did not go on the field trip?

   B. Did more or less than $\frac{1}{2}$ of the class go on the trip?

3. Mr. Henry's entire class went on the field trip. $\frac{5}{8}$ of Mr. Henry's class brought sandwiches for lunch. $\frac{2}{8}$ brought salads. The rest of the class brought fruit. What fraction of the class brought fruit?

TIMS Bit N

1. A. $\frac{1}{3}$

   B. more

2. A. $\frac{5}{8}$

   B. less

3. $\frac{1}{8}$

Money

1. What is the least number of coins (quarters, dimes, or nickels) needed to make $1.20?

2. What is the greatest number of quarters, dimes, or nickels needed to make 85 cents?

 Order Fractions

1. Which is greater $\frac{1}{12}$ or $\frac{1}{10}$? How did you decide?

2. Which is greater $\frac{3}{5}$ or $\frac{3}{8}$? How did you decide?

3. Which is greater $1\frac{1}{2}$ or $\frac{5}{4}$? How did you decide?

TIMS Task

1. 6 coins; 4 quarters and 2 dimes

2. 17 nickels

TIMS Bit

Students may use their fraction charts from Unit 12.

1. $\frac{1}{10}$; The whole is divided into fewer pieces, so each piece is larger.

2. $\frac{3}{5}$; The whole is divided into fewer pieces, so each piece is larger.

3. $1\frac{1}{2}$, $\frac{5}{4}$ is the same as $1\frac{1}{4}$. Since $\frac{1}{2}$ is larger than $\frac{1}{4}$, $1\frac{1}{2}$ is larger than $\frac{5}{4}$.

Favorite Sports

Mrs. Dewey conducted a survey to find out the favorite sports of the students in her class. John, Nicholas, and Ana each voted for a different sport—soccer, hockey, or baseball. Each of these three sports received either 9, 6, or 5 votes. Use the clues below to find out who voted for which sport and the number of votes each sport received.

Clue 1: John's sport received more votes than hockey.

Clue 2: Hockey is the favorite sport of the girl.

Clue 3: John's sport received fewer votes than baseball.

TIMS Challenge

John–soccer–6 votes

Nicholas–baseball–9 votes

Ana–hockey–5 votes

Allow students to try solving this problem in pairs or in groups of three. Students should extract all information from each clue before moving to the next clue. Encourage students to share their solution strategies.

After students are given an appropriate amount of time on their own, devising their own solution strategies, you might want to help them organize their information in a table like the following. As students read each clue, they write "yes" in a box when the information matches a person or score; they write "no" in a box if the information rules out a person or score.

	Soccer	Hockey	Baseball	9	6	5
John	yes	no	no	no	yes	no
Nicholas	no	no	yes	yes	no	no
Ana	no	yes	no	no	no	yes
9	no	no	yes			
6	yes	no	no			
5	no	yes	no			

Daily Practice and Problems: Bits for Lesson 1

A. Multiplication Practice
(URG p. 10)

Solve the following using a paper-and-pencil method or mental math. Estimate to make sure your answers are reasonable.

1. A. $46 \times 3 =$

   B. $76 \times 80 =$

   C. $92 \times 47 =$

   D. $25 \times 30 =$

2. Explain your estimation strategy for Question 1C.

C. Multiplication Facts Review
(URG p. 12)

A. $8 \times 4 =$ B. $7 \times 4 =$

C. $6 \times 7 =$ D. $7 \times 8 =$

E. $6 \times 8 =$ F. $4 \times 6 =$

E. Trumpet Practice (URG p. 13)

Ana's trumpet teacher told her to practice $\frac{3}{4}$ hour every day. Since 1 hour = 60 minutes, Ana used this number sentence to find the number of minutes she must practice each day: $\frac{3}{4} = \frac{?}{60}$.

1. Complete Ana's number sentence to find the number of minutes in $\frac{3}{4}$ hour.

2. Use Ana's method or your own strategies to find the following:

   A. How many minutes are in $\frac{1}{4}$ hour?

   B. How many minutes are in $\frac{1}{2}$ hour?

   C. How many minutes are in $\frac{1}{3}$ hour?

   D. How many minutes are in $\frac{1}{6}$ hour?

   E. How many minutes are in $1\frac{1}{4}$ hours?

   F. How many minutes are in 3.5 hours?

DPP Tasks are on page 37. Suggestions for using the DPPs are on page 37.

LESSON GUIDE

TV Survey

Estimated Class Sessions: 3

Students gather data in a survey to find the amount of television they watch. In an introductory session, they plan the survey. Then, they collect data over a four-day period as they continue with the lessons in this unit. Finally, when the four-day period is completed, students return to this activity in order to organize, graph, and analyze the data. Students solve multiplication and division problems using their *TV Survey* data. This activity provides one of the contexts for multiplication practice and an introduction to division.

Key Content

- Planning and conducting a survey.
- Collecting, organizing, graphing, and analyzing data.
- Binning data.
- Using multiplication and division to solve problems involving time.
- Averaging: finding the mean.

Key Vocabulary

binning
survey

Curriculum Sequence

Before This Unit

Surveys. In Unit 1, students collected, organized, and graphed survey data about the students in their classroom.

Materials List

Print Materials for Students

	Math Facts and Daily Practice and Problems	Activity	Homework
Student Books — Student Guide		*TV Survey* Pages 358–362	*TV Survey* Homework Section Pages 362–363
Student Books — Discovery Assignment Book		*Daily TV Time* Pages 219–220 and *How Much TV Do We Watch?* Page 221	Home Practice Parts 1 & 2 Page 213 and *Triangle Flash Cards: Last Six Facts* Page 217
Teacher Resources — Facts Resource Guide 🔘	DPP Items 13B–13D Use the *Triangle Flash Cards: Last Six Facts* to review the division facts for this group.		
Teacher Resources — Unit Resource Guide 🔘	DPP Items A–F Pages 10–14 🔘	*TV Survey: Letter Home* Page 40, 1 per student	
Teacher Resources — Generic Section 🔘		*Centimeter Graph Paper* and *Three-column Data Table,* 2 per student	

🔘 *available on Teacher Resource CD*

All Transparency Masters, Blackline Masters, and Assessment Blackline Masters in the Unit Resource Guide are on the Teacher Resource CD.

Supplies for Each Student

calculator
envelope for storing flash cards

Materials for the Teacher

Transparency of *Four-column Data Table* (Unit Resource Guide, Generic Section), several copies (see Before the Activity) or a laminated data table wall chart or large chart paper
Transparency of *Centimeter Graph Paper* (Unit Resource Guide, Generic Section)
Observational Assessment Record (Unit Resource Guide, Pages 7–8 and Teacher Resource CD)

Before the Activity

Send home the *TV Survey: Letter Home* Blackline Master before you begin the *TV Survey* activity. The data collection will last for four days. It will start the morning of the first day and continue to the evening of the fourth day. Therefore, if your data collection begins on Monday morning before school, send the letter home on the preceding Friday. On the letter, designate the four-day period of data collection.

After the four-day period of data collection is completed, each student will transfer his or her own *TV Survey* data onto a class transparency of the *Four-column Data Table*. Make enough copies of the data table to accommodate your classroom. An alternative is to make a four-column data table on chart paper or use a laminated data table wall chart. This one large data table will allow students to see everyone's data at one time.

Developing the Activity

TV Survey is divided into four parts:

1. The class discusses the procedures for collecting data, and students collect their own personal data over a four-day period. They record their data on the *Daily TV Time* Activity Pages in the *Discovery Assignment Book.*

2. Each student finds the total number of minutes he or she watched TV over the four-day period. Then, the average (mean) number of minutes and the average number of hours of TV time per day are calculated by each student.

3. Students transfer their data to a class data table. They organize the class data using the *How Much TV Do We Watch?* Activity Page in the *Discovery Assignment Book.*

4. Students graph the data on *Centimeter Graph Paper* and answer questions based on their graphs.

Part 1. Launching the Investigation and Collecting the Data

Begin a class discussion by reading the first page of the *TV Survey* Activity Pages in the *Student Guide*. Issues you may want to address include:

- the amount of time spent watching TV;
- the rules which govern television watching in different families;
- alternative activities students engage in other than watching TV.

Students will use the *Daily TV Time* Activity Pages in the *Discovery Assignment Book* to keep track of the amount of television they watch during the designated four-day period. This four-day period is long enough to capture students' habitual behavior, especially if the four days are regular school days— Monday through Thursday. Note that if data is collected over the weekend, and even on Friday evening, different viewing patterns may arise. Making predictions about viewing patterns and discussing the four-day period chosen will prove to be interesting.

Remind students to label each data table on their copies of the *Daily TV Time* Activity Pages with the correct day of the week so that each day of the four-day period is included. The data tables on the *Daily TV Time* Activity Pages include more information than is required merely to determine the amount of television watched. The analysis of this extra information may be of interest to you or some of your students.

Student Guide - Page 358

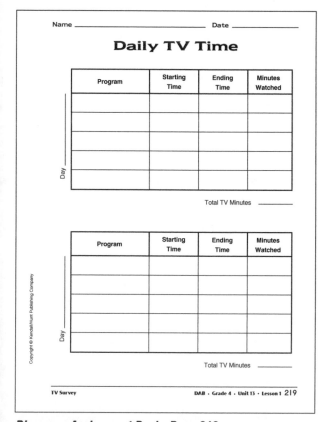

Discovery Assignment Book - Page 219

Discovery Assignment Book - Page 220

Daily TV Time

	Program	Starting Time	Ending Time	Minutes Watched
Thursday	Exploring Space	3:00	4:00	60
	Milo and Bob	4:00	4:30	30
	Power Troopers	6:00	6:30	30
	Take a Chance	6:30	7:00	30
	Treasure Search	8:00	8:45	45

Day

Average Number of Minutes per Day ___157.5___

Average Number of Hours per Day ___2.625___

Total TV Minutes ___195___

Total Number of Minutes for 4 Days ___630___

Figure 1: *A sample* Daily TV Time *data table*

TIMS Tip

Send the *Daily TV Time* Activity Pages home the night before data collection begins. Instruct students to keep the pages at home until the four-day period is completed.

TIMS Tip

Some students may forget to record the time spent watching TV in the morning hours before school. Students can record this information in their journals. They can later transfer the data to the *Daily TV Time* data tables which were sent home.

This survey analyzes the current habits of your students. Therefore, stress that students follow their usual television routines. A sample data table from the *Daily TV Time* Activity Pages is shown in Figure 1.

Before students collect the data *(Question 1),* discuss and agree on a set of rules for the data collection. Establishing rules and following them will help keep the survey fair. Discussing these rules, in a sense, is discussing the variables that will be held fixed. Use questions like the following to discuss the class rules for *TV Survey.*

- *On what four days will we record our TV data?* (Data collected over the weekend may show different results than data collected on school nights. Keeping the four-day period fixed for the entire class will help provide accurate data about your class's TV habits.)

- *If some of you collect data over a weekend and others record it over four school days, will this make the survey fair?* (No. The data may not accurately reflect the class's TV habits. You might predict that those students who record their data over a weekend will watch more TV. The four-day period chosen should be the same for all students.)

- *If several students recorded their parents' TV time instead of their own, would this be fair?* (No. We are studying fourth-graders' TV habits. We need to hold this variable fixed. Parents' data may differ from fourth-graders' data.)

- *How will we record the number of minutes watched?* (We recommend recording the time to the nearest 15 or 30 minutes. Calculations on the calculator, such as converting from minutes to hours, will result in "nice" decimals such as .5, .25, and .75. See Figure 1.)

- *Do we record the time we watch TV before and after school?* (Yes. This could easily be overlooked.)

- *If the TV is on but you are doing your homework, doing a jigsaw puzzle, chatting with a friend, or eating dinner, do you record this time spent as TV time?* (Reach a consensus on this type of question.)

- *If you are in a room and intend not to watch TV but an older brother turns it on, do you count it as TV time?* (Your class might say, "It depends." If you are engrossed in a book while your brother is watching TV, then, no. But if the program on TV catches your attention and you start watching it, look at the clock!)

- *Let's say you start to watch a show but you find out it's a rerun, so you turn the TV off. Do you record some TV time?* (Check the time. If 10 minutes have passed and your class is recording TV time to the nearest 15 minutes, you should record 15 minutes.)

- *Before school, you flick on the TV to catch the weather report. Do you count this?* (Students may disagree. Some might reason that if you time it right, the weather report is usually 2 to 3 minutes, so there would be no reason to record it. However, if you turn on the TV and watch 20 minutes of the news before the weather report is announced, then you should record this as TV time.)

- *Does playing video games count?* (Your class may or may not decide to count it as TV time. However, this question may be the topic of another survey.)

After discussing the rules of the data collection, ask students to make some predictions about the *TV Survey*. Have students record their predictions in their journals. After the data has been collected, you can compare their predictions to the actual results. Predict:

- *How many hours of TV do you think you will watch in four days?*

- *As a class, do you think we will watch more or less than 100 minutes of TV in four days? 1000 minutes?*

- *Do you watch the same amount of TV every day?*

- *On which day do you think we will watch the most TV? Why?*

TIMS Tip

Have students summarize the data collection procedures agreed upon by the class on the *TV Survey: Letter Home*.

Student Guide - Page 359

1. Record your data for a four-day period on the four tables on the *Daily TV Time* Activity Pages in the *Discovery Assignment Book*. One table should be used for each day. Irma's table for the fourth and final day is shown below.

Daily TV Time

	Program	Starting Time	Ending Time	Minutes Watched
Thursday	Exploring Space	3:00	4:00	60
	Milo and Bob	4:00	4:30	30
	Power Troopers	6:00	6:30	30
	Take a Chance	6:30	7:00	30
Day	Treasure Search	8:00	8:45	45

Average Number of Minutes per Day 157.5

Total TV Minutes 195

Average Number of Hours per Day _____

Total Number of Minutes for 4 Days 630

2. After the four-day period is complete, find and record the following information on your copy of the *Daily TV Time* Activity Page.
   A. The total number of minutes of TV time you watched over the four days
   B. The average (mean) number of minutes of TV time per day

Converting Average Number of Minutes to Average Number of Hours

3. Irma calculated that her average number of minutes of TV time per day is 157.5 minutes.
   A. Is her average daily TV time between 1 and 2 hours or between 2 and 3 hours? How did you decide?
   B. How many whole hours of TV, on average, did she watch per day?

Irma finds her average daily TV time in hours. She knows that 60 minutes are in 1 hour. She uses the calculator to do the following problem:

[1] [5] [7] [.] [5] [÷] [6] [0] [=] .

This is what the calculator window displayed: 2.625

TV Survey   SG · Grade 4 · Unit 13 · Lesson 1 359

- *Do you think your TV habits are different on school days than on weekends and holidays? Why or why not?*
- *On average, how many hours do you think you watch in one day?*
- *What average TV time per day is most common? less than 1 hour? 1–2 hours? 2–3 hours?*

Through the analysis of the data, we will explore many of these questions. However, Part 2 of this activity specifically focuses on the last question.

Part 2. Compiling the Raw Data

After the data collection is complete, your class will have a wealth of information to consider. You might begin the analysis of this information by asking in general what can be learned from the data. Many interesting facts are immediately evident in the data but to answer the questions posed before the data was collected and to check the predictions, the information needs to be condensed. Ask:

- *How can we organize the data so that we can answer the question—What average TV time per day is most common?*

Students may suggest that they first need to find and record the total number of minutes of TV each of them watched over the four-day period (*Question 2A* in the *Student Guide*). Then, each student should find the average number of minutes of TV time he or she watched per day *(Question 2B).* This information should be recorded on the *Daily TV Time* Activity Page in the *Discovery Assignment Book.* See Figure 1.

Advise students to use the mean as their average in this activity. The mean may provide a truer picture of the amount of TV watched during a 4-day period. Finding the mean will also give students practice with the division operation.

Discuss *Question 2B.* Dividing the total number of minutes by 4 will result in the average number of minutes of TV time watched per day. If students recorded their TV time to the nearest 15 or 30 minutes, division by four to find the average minutes of TV time per day will result in whole number answers or those that contain nice decimals such as .5, .25, and .75. Students may be familiar with these decimals and their fraction equivalents. For example, if a student watched 225 minutes in four days, 225 ÷ 4 = 56.25. This student's average TV time per day is between 56 and 57 minutes. Some students may recognize .25 as the same as one-fourth from their previous work in Unit 10 with decimals. 56.25 minutes can also be expressed as 56 minutes and 15 seconds, but students should be encouraged to write their average in decimal form since this data will be used in

Room 204's Raw Data

Name	Total TV Time for 4 Days in Minutes	Average TV Time per Day in Minutes	Average TV Time per Day in Hours
John	480	120	
Irma	630	157.5	
Roberto	165	41.25	
Maya	360	90	
Romesh	660	135	
Michael	315	78.75	
Tanya	240	60	

Figure 2: *A class data table*

further calculations. Answers in fractions or "minutes and seconds" will complicate these later calculations.

Display a transparency of a *Four-column Data Table*. Record each student's data in the first three columns as shown in Figure 2. The fourth column will be filled in after students have completed *Questions 3–5.*

At this point in the lesson, each student should know the average number of *minutes* of TV time he or she watched per day. Use *Questions 3–5* in the *Student Guide* to discuss strategies students may use to determine the average number of *hours* of TV time they watched per day. Here are two possible strategies students may use:

- Skip count by 60 minutes, mentally or on a calculator. For example, Irma averaged 157.5 minutes of TV time per day. To determine the number of hours in 157.5 minutes *(Question 3),* she can skip count by 60: 60 min. (1 hour), 120 min. (2 hours), 180 min. (3 hours). Since 157.5 minutes is between 120 and 180 minutes, Irma watched between 2 and 3 hours of TV time per day.

- Convert the minutes to hours by dividing by 60 on the calculator. The *Student Guide* pages demonstrate division by 60 on the calculator *(Question 4).* Irma uses a calculator to convert 157.5 minutes to hours. *Question 4* asks students to interpret the calculator's answer of "2.625." The 2 stands for 2 full hours. Simply noting that the number to the left of the decimal stands for *whole* hours and the numbers to the right stand for a *part* of an hour is sufficient at this time.

4. A. How many full hours did Irma watch on average per day?
   B. What does the ".625" tell you?
   C. Does the answer in the calculator display agree with your estimate in Question 3A?

5. Look at your average number of minutes of TV time per day.
   A. Is your average daily TV time more or less than 1 hour? More or less than 2 hours? More or less than 3 hours?
   B. Calculate your average number of hours of TV time per day and record it on your copy of the *Daily TV Time* Activity Page.

6. Compare your average daily TV time to the data reported in the newspaper article Mrs. Dewey shared with her class. (Remember, the newspaper article reported that students between the ages of 6 and 11 watch 3 hours of TV every day.) Did you watch more or less than 3 hours of TV each day of the survey?

Making a Class Data Table

7. Share your data with the class by recording it in a class data table like the one below.

The Class Data

Name	Total TV Time for 4 Days in Minutes	Average TV Time per Day in Minutes	Average TV Time per Day in Hours
John	480	120	2
Irma	630	157.5	2.625
Roberto	165	41.25	0.6875

Use your class data to answer Questions 8–10.

8. A. Who watched the most TV in your class?
   B. How many minutes did he or she watch TV?

9. A. Who watched the least TV in your class?
   B. How many minutes did he or she watch TV?

10. What can you learn from the class data table?

360 SG · Grade 4 · Unit 13 · Lesson 1   TV Survey

Student Guide - Page 360

How Much TV Do We Watch?

Name _____ Date _____

Average TV Time per Day (in hours)	Number of Students	
	Tallies	Total

TV Survey   DAB · Grade 4 · Unit 13 · Lesson 1   221

Discovery Assignment Book - Page 221

Content Note

Binning Data. We chose to use decimals in the bins as shown in Figure 3 since the use of whole numbers (e.g., 0–1, 1–2, 3–4, 5–6 hours) would have resulted in overlapping bins. Would a student who watched 1 hour of TV be categorized as having watched 0–1 hour of TV or 1–2 hours?

It is important for students to estimate the average TV time per day in hours before doing any calculations. Some students may have averaged only 60 minutes or less per day. When these students divide by 60 to find their average TV time per day in hours, the decimal should not surprise them. For example, a student who watched 41.25 minutes on average per day should realize that 41.25 minutes is less than 1 hour. Therefore, when 41.25 is divided by 60 on the calculator, the answer of 0.6875 should make sense. The "0" stands for 0 full hours.

Question 5 asks students to determine their average number of hours of TV time per day. Encourage students to first solve *Question 5A* without a calculator. Then, they may use a calculator to complete *Question 5B.* Discuss students' methods as well as the reasonableness of their answers. Students should record their answer to *Question 5B* on the *Daily TV Time* Activity Page as well as on the transparency of the class data. See Figures 1 and 2. After the data is compiled, ask students to complete *Questions 6–10* in the *Student Guide.* Discuss their answers to these questions.

Part 3. Binning the Data

After students have converted their average TV time per day to hours, ask:

*   *Have we answered the question—What average TV time per day is most common?*

Students may have a hard time coming to a conclusion. Students may scan the table trying to find students who watched the same amount of TV. The amount and variability of the data are great, but another problem may also be apparent. There might not be many exact matches. For example, one student may have watched TV for an average of 2 hours per day, another for 2.5 hours, and still another for 2.625 hours. This brings forth a good discussion about how to condense the data further to make it easier to analyze. Although 2 hours, 2.5 hours, and 2.625 hours are different times, all three are in fact between 2 and 3 hours. Therefore, **binning** the data, or categorizing the number of minutes into intervals such as 2–3 hours is appropriate. Students will use the table on the *How Much TV Do We Watch?* Activity Page in the *Discovery Assignment Book* to bin the class data.

How Much TV Do We Watch?

T Average TV Time per Day (in hours)	S Number of Students	
	Tallies	Total
0 – .99	⊬⊦⊦	5
1.00 – 1.99	⊬⊦⊦ IIII	9
2.00 – 2.99	III	3
3.00 – 3.99	IIII	4
4.00 – 4.99	⊬⊦⊦	5
5.00 – 5.99		0
6.00 – 6.99	I	1
7.00 – 7.99	II	2

Figure 3: *Binning data on the* How Much TV Do We Watch? *Activity Page*

Have students fill in the variables in the column headings on the *How Much TV Do We Watch?* Activity Page as shown in Figure 3. Before starting to bin the data (*Question 11* in the *Student Guide*), ask:

- *What are the two main variables we are studying?" (Question 12)* (*T*, TV Time in Hours and *S*, Number of Students.)

Students should fill in the left-hand column with appropriate bins or categories as shown in Figure 3. The class can initially start with bins up to "4.00–4.99 hours" and then add bins if necessary (e.g., 5.00–5.99, 6.00–6.99, etc.).

Transfer the table on the *How Much TV Do We Watch?* Activity Page onto the chalkboard or chart paper. Display on the overhead the class data that was recorded earlier on transparencies of the *Four-column Data Table*. As students tell you which bin they belong in, you and the class can discuss whether their choice seems appropriate. The students may make tallies for their classmates on their own copy of the *How Much TV Do We Watch?* Activity Page as well.

11. Look at the last column in your class data table. Find out how many students' average daily TV time was between 0 and 1 hour, between 1 and 2 hours, between 2 and 3 hours, etc. Complete a table like the one below.

How Much TV Do We Watch?

T Average TV Time per Day (in hours)	S Number of Students	
	Tallies	Total
0 – .99	⊬⊦⊦	
1.00 – 1.99	III\	
2.00 – 2.99	II	
3.00 – 3.99	IIII	
4.00 – 4.99	I	

12. What are the two main variables we are studying?

Graph

13. Make a bar graph on *Centimeter Graph Paper* using your class television data. Label the horizontal axis with *T*, TV Time in Hours, and the vertical axis with *S*, Number of Students.

14. How many students in your class averaged between 0 and 1 hour of TV per day?

15. What average TV time is most common?

16. Describe the graph. What does the graph tell you about the amount of TV the students in your class watched?

Extension

Follow-up Survey. One month later, collect data over four days one more time. Make a data table and graph. Compare your data to the first TV Survey you completed. See if the TV Survey helped to change your habits.

Student Guide - Page 361

Bar Graphs. Notice that the bars in the graph in Figure 4 are drawn in the spaces rather than on the vertical lines. Bars are drawn on the line if they represent only one value. In this case, the bar above "1–2" may include not only a student who watched on average 1 hour of TV per day, but also a student who watched 1 hour and 15 minutes of TV (1.25 hours), 1 hour and 30 minutes (1.5 hours), 1 hour and 45 minutes (1.75 hours), etc. Since these values are between 1 and 2 hours, the bar goes between 1 and 2. This data corresponds to the data in the table for the row labeled 1.00–1.99. Similarly, the bar in the interval between 2 and 3 represents the data in the row labeled 2.00–2.99. This bar shows the number of students who watched between 2 and 3 hours, including those students who watched exactly 2 hours, but not those who watched exactly 3 hours.

Journal Prompt

Write a letter to your parents describing the results of the *TV Survey.* What does the survey tell you about TV habits of fourth-graders in your class?

Part 4. Graphing and Analyzing the Results

Making a bar graph of the binned data will give the class yet another representation of their data. Students can make their graphs on *Centimeter Graph Paper (Question 13).* The horizontal axis should be labeled, *T,* TV Time (in Hours). The vertical axis should be labeled, *S,* Number of Students. See Figure 4 for a sample graph based on the data in Figure 3.

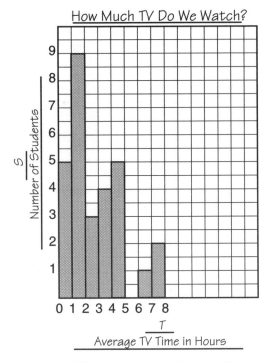

Figure 4: *Sample bar graph*

After making their graphs, students complete *Questions 14–16.* Students may answer *Questions 14–15* using either their data tables or their graphs. In *Question 15,* students answer the question that was posed earlier—What average TV time per day was most common? In the table in Figure 3, most students watched, on average, between 1 and 2 hours of TV per day.

Question 16 asks students to describe the graph. Looking at the graph in Figure 4, students might say:

- Most of us watched on average somewhere between 0 and 5 hours per day.

- First the graph bars go up. A lot of us averaged between 0 and 2 hours of TV per day. Then the bars go down. Fewer students averaged between 2 and 3 hours. Finally, hardly anyone watched more than 5 hours of TV per day.

Suggestions for Teaching the Lesson

Math Facts

- DPP Task B reminds students to review the division facts for the last six facts with *Triangle Flash Cards*. Items C and D provide practice with the multiplication and division facts for this group.

- Part 1 of the Home Practice reminds students to practice division facts using their *Triangle Flash Cards: Last Six Facts*.

Homework and Practice

- Assign the problems in the Homework section in the *Student Guide*. **Questions 1–6** provide practice with adding, subtracting, and converting minutes to hours. **Questions 7–10** ask students to bin data, make a bar graph, and analyze the results. You may wish to assign the homework over two nights. Each student needs one copy of *Centimeter Graph Paper* and two copies of a *Three-column Data Table* to complete the homework.

- DPP Bit A provides multiplication practice using paper and pencil, estimation, and mental math.

- Bit E and Task F practice converting between hours and minutes. Students will use this skill in their analysis of the *TV Survey* data.

- Home Practice Part 2 is a set of word problems that asks students to interpret remainders.

Answers for Part 2 of the Home Practice may be found in the Answer Key at the end of this lesson and at the end of this unit.

Name _____ Date _____

Triangle Flash Cards: Last Six Facts

- Work with a partner. Each partner cuts out the flash cards.
- To quiz you on a division fact, your partner covers the number in the square. Solve a division fact with the two uncovered numbers.
- Divide the used cards into three piles: those that you know and can answer quickly, those that you can figure out, and those that you need to learn.
- Practice the last two piles again. Then, make a list of the facts you need to practice at home.
- Go through the cards again. This time your partner covers the numbers in the circles.
- Sort the cards into the three piles. Make a list of the facts you need to practice at home.
- Repeat the directions for your partner.

DIVISION   DAB · Grade 4 · Unit 13   217

Discovery Assignment book - Page 217

Daily Practice and Problems: Tasks for Lesson 1

B. Task: The Last Six Facts (URG p. 11)

With a partner, use your *Triangle Flash Cards: Last Six Facts* to quiz each other on the related division facts for the last six multiplication facts ($24 \div 6$, $24 \div 4$; $28 \div 7$, $28 \div 4$, $32 \div 8$, $32 \div 4$, $42 \div 7$, $42 \div 6$, $48 \div 8$, $48 \div 6$, $56 \div 8$, $56 \div 7$). Ask your partner first to cover the numbers in the squares. Use the two uncovered numbers to solve a division fact. Then, ask your partner to cover the numbers in the circles. Use the uncovered numbers to solve a division fact.

After each time through the cards, separate them into three piles: those facts you know and can answer quickly, those that you can figure out with a strategy, and those that you need to learn. Practice the last two piles again and then make a list of the facts you need to practice at home for homework.

Circle the facts you know and can answer quickly on your *Division Facts I Know* chart.

D. Task: Fact Families for × and ÷ (URG p. 12)

The following four facts belong to the same fact family.

$$4 \times 6 = 24 \qquad 6 \times 4 = 24$$

$$24 \div 6 = 4 \qquad 24 \div 4 = 6$$

Solve each fact. Then, name three other facts that are in the same fact family.

A. $28 \div 7 =$

B. $7 \times 8 =$

C. $7 \times 6 =$

D. $32 \div 4 =$

E. $8 \times 6 =$

F. Task: TV Survey Data
(URG p. 14)

1. Last night, Shannon watched 3 hours of TV. How many minutes is 3 hours?

2. Maya watched 2.5 hours of TV. How many minutes is this?

3. Nicholas watched $2\frac{1}{4}$ hours of TV. How many minutes is this?

4. How many minutes did these three students watch in all? How many hours?

TV Time vs. Reading Time. Collect data comparing the number of minutes you watch TV to the number of minutes you read every day. Graph and discuss your results. Give up television for four days and collect data on your reading habits within those four days. Discuss your results.

Homework

You will need a calculator, a *Three-Column Data Table*, and *Centimeter Graph Paper* to complete the homework.

On Monday, Mrs. Dewey's class started their data collection for TV Survey. The data collection continued through Thursday evening. On Friday, the students shared their data by combining it all on one large data table. A piece of their class data table is shown below.

The Class Data

Name and Group Number		Average TV Time per Day in Minutes	Average TV Time per Day in Hours
Ming	(Group 7)	240	
Shannon	(Group 7)	135	
Ana	(Group 7)	390	
Luis	(Group 7)	195	
Nicholas	(Group 8)	45	
Lee Yah	(Group 8)	210	
Jacob	(Group 8)	105	
Nila	(Group 8)	180	

Mrs. Dewey's students sit in groups of four. The students listed in the table above are in Groups 7 and 8.

1. Who watched more television, Group 7 or Group 8? How did you decide?

2. How many minutes of television did Group 7 watch in all?

Student Guide - Page 362

3. How many minutes of television did Group 8 watch in all?

4. How many more minutes of television did Ana watch than Shannon?

5. Lee Yah watched about twice as much television as another student. Who? How did you decide?

6. Copy the previous data table onto a *Three-column Data Table*. Find the number of hours each student watched TV. Fill in the third column with your findings.

7. Each student in Groups 1 through 6 came to the overhead and placed a tally for themselves as shown in the following data table. Copy this data table onto a copy of a *Three-column Data Table*. Add the data for the students in Groups 7 and 8 to the table using tallies. Then, total the tallies.

How Much TV Do We Watch?

Average TV Time per Day (in hours)	Number of Students	
	Tallies	Total
0 – .99	̶H̶H̶	
1.00 – 1.99	IIII	
2.00 – 2.99	III	
3.00 – 3.99		
4.00 – 4.99	I	
5.00 – 5.99		
6.00 – 6.99	I	
7.00 – 7.99		

8. What amount of TV viewing is most common in Mrs. Dewey's class?

9. Graph all of Room 204's data on *Centimeter Graph Paper*.

10. Describe the graph. What does it tell you about the amount of TV the students in Room 204 watched?

Student Guide - Page 363

Name _____ Date _____

Unit 13: Home Practice

Part 1 *Triangle Flash Cards: Last Six Facts*
Study for the quiz on the division facts for the last six facts (24 ÷ 6, 24 ÷ 4, 28 ÷ 7, 28 ÷ 4, 32 ÷ 8, 32 ÷ 4, 42 ÷ 7, 42 ÷ 6, 48 ÷ 8, 48 ÷ 6, 56 ÷ 8, 56 ÷ 7). Take home your *Triangle Flash Cards* and your list of facts you need to study.

Here's how to use the flash cards. Ask a family member to choose one flash card at a time. Your partner should cover the corner containing either the square or the circle. This number will be the answer to a division fact. Solve a division fact with the two uncovered numbers.

Your teacher will tell you when the quiz on these facts will be. Remember to study only those facts you cannot answer correctly and quickly.

Part 2 **Working with Remainders**
Show how you solved each of the following problems. Explain how any remainders affected your answer.

1. Nine cereal boxes fit into one crate. How many crates are needed for 30 boxes of cereal?

2. Twenty-one children try out for two teams. The children decided that anyone who is not selected will be an umpire. There are three umpires. How many children are on each of the two teams?

3. Mrs. Roberts collects a total of $273 from the 90 students who are going on a field trip. Each student brings in $3. Is the total of $273 the correct amount? Explain.

4. Irma wants to read her 453-page book in 9 days. If she reads about the same number of pages each night, how many should she read a night?

Discovery Assignment Book - Page 213

Suggestions for Teaching the Lesson (*continued*)

Assessment

Use the *Observational Assessment Record* to document students' abilities to collect, organize, graph, and analyze data.

Extension

The *TV Survey* Activity Pages in the *Student Guide* offer two extensions. Assign one of these to students who will benefit from an independent assignment using data collection and graphing. If students choose to do a follow-up survey, they should remember the class rules that students developed for the original investigation. Remind students to collect data over the same four-day period, whether it was four school nights or over the weekend. Keeping the variables fixed will allow them to compare their results to the original survey. When students finish the assignment, they can present their findings to their classmates.

AT A GLANCE

Math Facts and Daily Practice and Problems

DPP Bit A provides multiplication practice. Items B, C, and D provide multiplication and division practice with the last six facts. Items E and F ask students to convert hours to minutes.

Part 1. Launching the Investigation and Collecting the Data

1. Send home copies of the *TV Survey: Letter Home* Blackline Master from the *Unit Resource Guide.*
2. Read the first page of the *TV Survey* Activity Pages in the *Student Guide.*
3. Discuss rules for collecting data on the students' TV viewing time.
4. The class makes predictions in their journals about what the data will show.
5. Students use the *Daily TV Time* Activity Pages in the *Discovery Assignment Book* to keep track of the television they watch during a designated four-day period. *(Question 1)*

Part 2. Compiling the Raw Data

1. Discuss in general what can be learned from the class data.
2. Discuss how to organize the data to answer the question, *"What average TV time per day is most common?"*
3. Each student finds his or her individual total in minutes for the four-day period. Each student also finds his or her average number of minutes of TV time per day. Students record both pieces of data on the *Daily TV Time* Activity Pages. *(Question 2)*
4. Record students' individual data on transparencies of the *Four-column Data Table.*
5. Students convert the average number of minutes they watched per day to hours. Then, they share this data with the class. *(Questions 3–10)*

Part 3. Binning the Data

As a class, students bin the data using the table on the *How Much TV Do We Watch?* Activity Page in the *Discovery Assignment Book. (Questions 11–12)*

Part 4. Graphing and Analyzing the Results

1. Students make a bar graph of the data in the table on the *How Much TV Do We Watch?* Activity Page. *(Question 13)*
2. Students complete *Questions 14–16* on the *TV Survey* Activity Pages.

Homework

1. Students complete homework *Questions 1–10* in the *Student Guide.*
2. Assign Parts 1 and 2 of the Home Practice in the *Discovery Assignment Book.*

Assessment

Document students' abilities to collect, organize, graph, and analyze data on the *Observational Assessment Record.*

Notes:

TV Survey: Letter Home

Dear Family Member:

Our class will soon be conducting a survey on the amount of television fourth-graders watch. Each student in the class will collect his or her own personal data. Then, we will compile and graph the class data. Finally, we will analyze the results of the survey and use the data to solve problems involving time, multiplication, and division.

We need your help to make this project succeed. Accurate data is required and that data must be gathered at home. Your child will record the number of minutes he or she watches TV at home every day for four days. In class, we have discussed procedures for record-keeping.

The data collection will begin the morning of _____

and will continue through the evening of _____ .

Your child has a form with data tables for keeping track of the amount of TV he or she watches. We encourage you to review your child's record-keeping. Since this is a survey, we ask that you follow your normal routines for watching television.

If you have any questions, please feel free to contact me at school.

Sincerely,

_____

Student Guide

Questions 1–16 (SG pp. 359–361)

1. *

2. *Answers will vary. Students record answers on their *Daily TV Time* Activity Page.

3. **A.** *Between 2 and 3 hours. Possible solution: Skip count by 60s to 180.

   B. 2 whole hours

4. **A.** *2 full hours

   B. *Numbers to the right of the decimal stand for part of an hour.

   C. Answers will vary.

5. *

6.–10. Answers will vary.

11. *

12. *T, TV Time (in Hours) and S, Number of Students

13. *See sample graph in Lesson Guide.

14. Answers will vary. Based on sample graph, 5 students.

15. Answers will vary. Based on sample graph, between 1 and 2 hrs.

16. *Answers will vary.

Homework (SG pp. 362–363)

Questions 1–10

1. Group 7; Total TV Time for Group 7 = 240 + 135 + 390 + 195 = 960 min and Total TV Time for Group 8 = 45 + 210 + 105 + 180 = 540 min.

2. 960 minutes

3. 540 minutes

4. 255 minutes more

5. Jacob; $105 \times 2 = 210$ min

6.

Name and Group Number		Average TV Time per Day in Minutes	Average TV Time per Day in Hours
Ming	(Group 7)	240	4
Shannon	(Group 7)	135	2.25
Ana	(Group 7)	390	6.5
Luis	(Group 7)	195	3.25
Nicholas	(Group 8)	45	0.75
Lee Yah	(Group 8)	210	3.5
Jacob	(Group 8)	105	1.75
Nila	(Group 8)	180	3

7.

T Average TV Time per Day (in hours)	S Number of Students	
	Tallies	Total
0 – .99	⊥⊥⊥ l	6
1.00 – 1.99	⊥⊥⊥	5
2.00 – 2.99	llll	4
3.00 – 3.99	lll	3
4.00 – 4.99	ll	2
5.00 – 5.99		0
6.00 – 6.99	ll	2

8. less than 1 hour

---

*Answers and/or discussion are included in the Lesson Guide.

**Answers for all the Home Practice in the *Discovery Assignment Book* are at the end of the unit.

9.

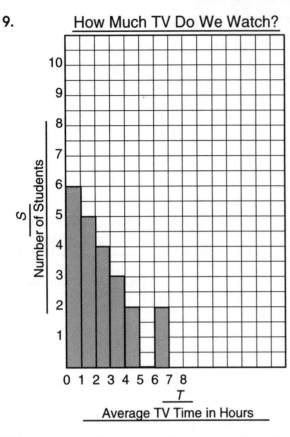

How Much TV Do We Watch?

Number of Students S

Average TV Time in Hours T

Discovery Assignment Book

**Home Practice (DAB p. 213)

Part 2. Working with Remainders

Questions 1–4

Explanations will vary.

1. 4 crates; $30 \div 9 = 3$ crates R3 boxes. The remainder tells us that one more crate or 10 crates are needed to ship all the boxes.

2. $21 \div 2 = 18$ R3; 9 children on 2 teams with 3 umpires.

3. No, the correct answer should be $90 \times 3 = \$270$. $\$273 - \$270 = \$3$; Mrs. Roberts collected $3.00 too much.

4. About 50 pages. Students can round 453 to 450. $450 \div 9 = 50$ pages.

10. Answers will vary. Possible answer: The tallest bars are to the left which means most students watched a small number of hours of TV.

*Answers and/or discussion are included in the Lesson Guide.

**Answers for all the Home Practice in the *Discovery Assignment Book* are at the end of the unit.

LESSON GUIDE

Division

Estimated Class Sessions: 3

Students are introduced to long division by modeling with base-ten pieces. They discuss division symbols and the forgiving method for long division. Problems involve dividing one-digit numbers into two-digit numbers.

Key Content

- Representing division using base-ten pieces.
- Connecting the symbols $\overline{)}$ and $\div$ with division situations.
- Dividing with one-digit divisors and two-digit dividends using paper and pencil.
- Interpreting remainders.
- Estimating quotients.

Key Vocabulary

dividend
forgiving method for division
quotient
remainder

Daily Practice and Problems: Bits for Lesson 2

G. Skip Counting by 6 and 60
(URG p. 14)

1. Skip count by 6s from 6 to 60.
   Start this way: 6, 12, 18, . . .

2. Skip count by 60s from 60 to 600.
   Start this way: 60, 120, 180, . . .

I. More TV Survey Data
(URG p. 15)

Linda watched 45 minutes of TV on Monday, 135 minutes on Tuesday, and 30 minutes on Wednesday. She did not watch TV on Thursday.

1. Use a calculator to find the mean number of minutes of TV Linda watched each day.

2. Give a quick estimate for the median number of minutes watched.

K. Related Division Facts (URG p. 17)

Solve each fact. Then, name the other division fact in the same fact family.

A. $56 \div 8 =$

B. $32 \div 4 =$

C. $42 \div 7 =$

D. $24 \div 4 =$

E. $48 \div 6 =$

F. $28 \div 7 =$

DPP Tasks are on page 50. Suggestions for using the DPPs are on page 50.

Curriculum Sequence

Before This Unit

Students studied division in Unit 7 and Unit 19 of third grade. In fourth grade, students studied divisibility rules in Unit 7 and solved division problems in Unit 4 and in the DPP.

Materials List

Print Materials for Students

	Math Facts and Daily Practice and Problems	Activity	Homework
Student Guide		*Division* Pages 364–368	*Division* Homework Section Pages 368–370
Discovery Assignment Book			Home Practice Parts 5 & 6 Page 215
Facts Resource Guide ⊙	DPP Items 13H & 13K		
Unit Resource Guide	DPP Items G–L Pages 14–17 ⊙		

⊙ *available on Teacher Resource CD*

All Transparency Masters, Blackline Masters, and Assessment Blackline Masters in the Unit Resource Guide are on the Teacher Resource CD.

Supplies for Each Student Pair

set of base-ten pieces: 2 packs, 14 flats, 30 skinnies, 50 bits

Materials for the Teacher

Observational Assessment Record (Unit Resource Guide, Pages 7–8 and Teacher Resource CD)
overhead base-ten pieces, optional

Developing the Activity

Part 1. Modeling Division

Begin class discussion by posing the following problem:

- *Ana and Roberto have 57 marbles to share. How many marbles should each get if they are divided fairly?*

- *Will all of the 57 marbles be shared between the two children if each child gets the same amount?* (Since 2 does not divide 57 evenly, Ana and Roberto must decide what to do with the remaining marble.)

- *Estimate the number of marbles that each child will get.* (One strategy is to say that 57 is close to 60. Each child should get about, but less than, 30 marbles each.)

Model 57 using the base-ten pieces. Use 5 skinnies and 7 bits as shown in Figure 5. Remind students that in this lesson, the bit is one.

Figure 5: *Representing 57 with base-ten pieces*

Have students use their base-ten pieces to model along with you. They may suggest first passing out the bits, which is fine. Another way is to begin with the skinnies. Ana and Roberto each get 2 skinnies as shown in Figure 6.

Figure 6: *Distributing the skinnies*

Ask:

- *How many marbles are represented by 2 skinnies?* (20)

- *How can we divide up the remaining skinny and the 7 bits?*

The remaining skinny can be divided into 10 bits, giving 17 bits altogether as shown in Figure 7.

Figure 7: *Regrouping*

TIMS Tip

Students will need to work in groups of four to share base-ten pieces.

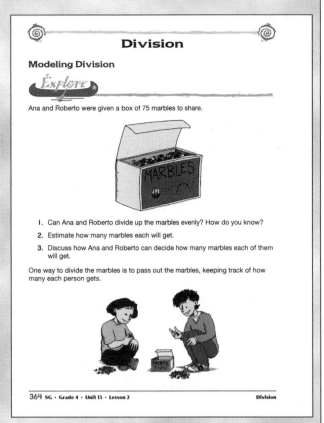

Student Guide - Page 364

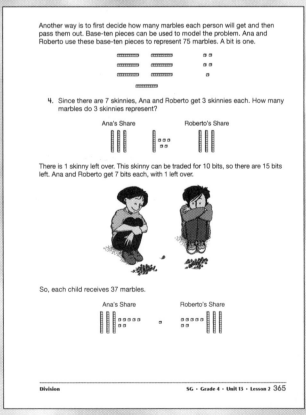

Student Guide - Page 365

Since there are 17 bits, each child gets 8 bits, leaving 1 bit, as shown in Figure 8.

Figure 8: *Completing the distribution*

Discuss with students that Ana and Roberto each got 28 marbles. One marble remained. We say 57 divided by 2 is 28 with remainder 1. Explain to children that the word **remainder** means the amount that could not be distributed evenly, that is, the amount left over. You can point out that if we deal with objects that can be cut up, like cookies, then the remainder can be shared equally.

Do several more modeling problems, providing as much guidance as needed. You can use base-ten shorthand instead of the pieces so that the children move from the concrete representation to the pictorial. Some example problems to model together include:

- $56 \div 3$
- $84 \div 4$
- $65 \div 5$
- $93 \div 6$

For each problem, ask students to estimate their answers first. After completing the problem, have them compare their estimate to their answer to make sure the answer is reasonable.

Discuss the different division symbols. Students have seen the division symbol ($\div$) before, but this symbol ($\overline{)}\,$) may be new. Instead of writing "75 divided by 8," we can write $8\overline{)75}$ or $75 \div 8$ instead.

Write several problems on the board and have students make up stories that match the problems and then solve the problems using the base-ten pieces or base-ten shorthand. For each problem, ask students to explain what the remainder means. Some possible problems:

- $69 \div 7$
- $9 \div 4$
- $3\overline{)47}$

Ask students to do the Modeling Division section of the *Division* Activity Pages in the *Student Guide* in pairs or groups. *Questions 1–4* discuss a problem similar to the one done in class. You can use this opportunity to walk around the room and listen to the groups discussing the problems, to see how students comprehend division. *Questions 5–6* ask students to write stories for two division problems.

Questions 1–6 in the Homework section should be assigned at this point in the lesson.

Part 2. The Forgiving Method

Explain to students that there are many ways of doing division. You are going to show them a method that uses only pencil and paper. This method is called the Forgiving Method.

Using the forgiving method consists of making estimates about the **quotient,** the answer to the division problem.

Use the context of dividing marbles to divide 74 by 3. We write:

$$3\overline{)74}$$

The first step is to estimate the number of times 3 divides 74. Suggest students think in terms of base-ten pieces: 7 skinnies and 4 bits need to be divided into 3 groups. Some students may make a good guess, like 20. Others may choose much smaller numbers or larger numbers. If a smaller number is chosen, this is fine. The only time we need to erase is if we choose too high. Also, suggest to students that they choose convenient numbers at the beginning of a problem. For example, numbers that end in zeros so that the multiplication is easy.

Say we chose 10. Then, since $3 \times 10 = 30$, we have taken care of 30 of the marbles:

$$
\begin{array}{r}
3 \overline{)\ 74} \\
-\ 30 \\
\hline
44
\end{array}
\quad 10
$$

Now we ask how many times 3 divides 44 (or 4 skinnies and 4 bits need to be distributed into 3 groups). We can choose 10 again and write:

$$
\begin{array}{r}
3 \overline{)\ 74} \\
-\ 30 \\
\hline
44 \\
-\ 30 \\
\hline
14
\end{array}
\quad
\begin{array}{l}
10 \\
\\
10
\end{array}
$$

Content Note

Forgiving Method. This method of division is called the forgiving method because it "forgives" estimates that are too low. It is similar to the traditional method if the best estimate is taken at each step. For more information, see the Background of this unit and the TIMS Tutor: *Arithmetic* in the *Teacher Implementation Guide.*

Since 3 goes into 14 a total of 4 times we write:

$$
\begin{array}{r|l}
3\overline{)\ 74} & \\
-\ 30 & 10 \\
\hline
44 & \\
-\ 30 & 10 \\
\hline
14 & \\
-\ 12 & 4 \\
\hline
2 & \\
\end{array}
$$

Since 3 does not divide 2, 2 is the remainder. That is, 2 marbles are left over. We add up the number of 3s we took away: $10 + 10 + 4 = 24$.

Thus, 74 divided by 3 is 24 with remainder 2. We finish the problem by writing the quotient and remainder on top:

$$
\begin{array}{r|l}
24\ \text{R2} & \\
3\overline{)\ 74} & \\
-\ 30 & 10 \\
\hline
44 & \\
-\ 30 & 10 \\
\hline
14 & \\
-\ 12 & 4 \\
\hline
2 & \\
\end{array}
$$

Another way to do this problem using the forgiving method:

$$
\begin{array}{r|l}
24\ \text{R2} & \\
3\overline{)\ 74} & \\
-\ 60 & 20 \\
\hline
14 & \\
-\ 12 & 4 \\
\hline
2 & \\
\end{array}
$$

Note that making the best estimates results in the same number of steps as the traditional method.

Practice several more problems with students. If some of them have learned the traditional method, point out to them that the forgiving method is really very much the same. The only difference is that you do not need to find the maximum number immediately. In other words, the forgiving method allows you to choose small. If you choose too big, you have to erase just as with the traditional method. Encourage students to make good estimates before they begin, to keep the length of the problems at a minimum.

Content Note

Remainders. While it is correct to say that the remainder is 0 for a problem such as 24 divided by 3, we feel it is fine to say "there is no remainder," since there is nothing left to distribute.

TIMS Tip

The forgiving method is presented as one possible algorithm to teach. If your students understand the traditional method or any other method and find it easy to work with, they should be allowed to continue using it.

Questions 7–8 in The Forgiving Method section in the *Student Guide* discuss another problem using the forgiving method. Go through the example with students.

Questions 9–10 provide an opportunity to practice the forgiving method in groups and discuss remainders. For *Question 9* students need to find how many groups (cabins) will be needed if there are 95 boys and 7 boys fit in a cabin. Since $95 \div 7 = 13$ R4, they will need 14 cabins. The quotient 13 tells us that we can completely fill 13 cabins. The remainder 4 tells us that another cabin is needed since 4 boys still need a cabin. One arrangement is to have 13 cabins with 7 boys and 1 cabin with 4 boys. Another arrangement is to have 11 cabins with 7 boys, 3 cabins with 6 boys. The remaining arrangement has 12 cabins with 7 boys, 1 cabin with 6 boys, and 1 cabin with 5 boys.

For *Question 10* 43 boys have to be distributed as equally as possible among the 9 available tents. Since $43 \div 9 = 4$ R7, we can interpret this as meaning put 4 boys in each of the 9 tents. This takes care of 36 boys. There are 7 boys left to distribute to the 9 tents. To avoid overcrowding any tent, one extra boy should be placed in 7 of the tents. Thus, 7 tents will have 5 boys and 2 tents will have 4 boys.

There are several ways to write 75 divided by 2 using math symbols. Here are 2 ways:

$$2\overline{)75} \qquad 75 \div 2$$

Write a story for each of the problems, Questions 5–6, and then find the answer. Be sure to explain what any remainders mean.

5. $6\overline{)78}$ 　　　　　　　6. $93 \div 4$

The Forgiving Method

Keenya said she had a third way of solving 75 divided by 2 using paper and pencil. We call this the **forgiving method.** Keenya wrote:

$$2\overline{)75}$$

Keenya then estimated how many marbles she thought each child would get. Her first estimate was 20 each. Since each child gets 20, and $2 \times 20 = 40$, 40 marbles are taken care of. Keenya wrote:

$$
\begin{array}{r}
2\overline{)75} \\
-40 \;|\;20 \\
\hline
35
\end{array}
$$

Keenya has 35 marbles left to pass out.

7. How many marbles should she give each child now? What is a good estimate?

Keenya decided to give each child 10 more marbles.

8. Why did Keenya know that giving 20 more marbles to each child is too much?

She wrote:

$$
\begin{array}{r}
2\overline{)75} \\
-40\;|\;20 \\
\hline
35 \\
-20\;|\;10 \\
\hline
15
\end{array}
$$

Student Guide - Page 366

Keenya then chose 7. Since $2 \times 7 = 14$, she wrote:

$$
\begin{array}{r}
2\overline{)75} \\
-40\;|\;20 \\
\hline
35 \\
-20\;|\;10 \\
\hline
15 \\
-14\;|\;7 \\
\hline
1
\end{array}
$$

Keenya saw that she could not divide further. She added up $20 + 10 + 7 = 37$. This is the number of times 2 divides 75. She finished the problem by writing the quotient on top: 37 and remainder, 1.

$$
\begin{array}{r}
37\;R1 \\
2\overline{)75} \\
-40\;|\;20 \\
\hline
35 \\
-20\;|\;10 \\
\hline
15 \\
-14\;|\;7 \\
\hline
1
\end{array}
$$

Here is another way to do this problem using the forgiving method.

$$
\begin{array}{r}
37\;R1 \\
2\overline{)75} \\
-60\;|\;30 \\
\hline
15 \\
-14\;|\;7 \\
\hline
1
\end{array}
$$

Student Guide - Page 367

Journal Prompt

Write a story for the division sentence $96 \div 7$. Solve the problem. Explain any remainder.

The Boys' Wilderness Club from Bessie Coleman School is going camping.

9. The younger boys are sleeping in cabins. Each cabin holds 7 people. If there are 95 younger boys, how many cabins will be needed?
   A. Estimate the number of cabins. Will the number of cabins be more than 10? more than 20? more than 15?
   B. Divide 95 by 7.
   C. What does the quotient mean?
   D. What does the remainder mean?
   E. How many boys will sleep in each cabin?
   F. Is there another way to arrange the number of boys in each cabin?

10. The older boys in the Wilderness Club want to sleep in tents. The club has 9 tents. There are 43 older boys. How many boys can sleep in each tent so that no tent is overcrowded?
   A. Estimate the number of boys in each tent.
   B. Solve the problem and explain your reasoning.

Solve the following problems using the forgiving method or mental math. Record both the quotient and remainder for your final answer. Estimate to be sure your answer is reasonable.

11. $49 \div 3$ 　　12. $92 \div 4$ 　　13. $56 \div 7$ 　　14. $89 \div 6$

Homework

Use base-ten shorthand to model the two story problems below. Remember to describe how to use the remainder.

1. A group of campers are setting up tents. Each tent needs 6 poles. There are 32 poles in the box. How many tents can be set up?

Student Guide - Page 368

H. Task: Multiples of 10 and 100 (URG p. 15)

Solve each pair of related number sentences.

A. $4 \times 80 =$ and $320 \div 4 =$

B. $40 \times 6 =$ and $240 \div 40 =$

C. $70 \times 4 =$ and $280 \div 70 =$

D. $60 \times 7 =$ and $420 \div 7 =$

E. $8 \times 70 =$ and $560 \div 70 =$

F. $80 \times 60 =$ and $4800 \div 80 =$

J. Task: Moving Out (URG p. 16)

Use base-ten pieces or shorthand to solve the following. Explain any remainders.

1. Ming is helping his mother pack the books on the living room bookshelves. There are 46 books to pack and 4 boxes. How many books can Ming pack in each box?

2. Ming's mother hired a moving company. A father and two sons evenly split their pay of $225. How much did each person earn?

L. Task: Draw One Whole
(URG p. 17)

You will need some pattern blocks to complete this item.

1. If the shape below is one whole, draw $\frac{1}{4}$.

2. Draw $1\frac{1}{2}$.

Suggestions for Teaching the Lesson

Math Facts

DPP Task H provides practice with multiplication and division facts using multiples of 10. Bit K uses fact families to practice the division facts for the last six facts.

Homework and Practice

- Assign **Questions 1–6** in the Homework section of the *Student Guide* after Part 1 of the lesson. Discuss the homework in class the next day. Make sure students can interpret the remainders. In **Question 1,** 5 tents can be set up since $32 \div 6 = 5$ R2. The 2 represents the extra poles. Students may approach **Question 2** in different ways. Since 22 divided by 6 is 3 R4, children may say that they first put 3 people into each boat. Then, the 4 remaining people are put into boats so that every one is taken care of. Another way to solve the problem is to divide 22 by 4, which gives the number of boats needed. Since $22 \div 4 = 5$ R2, the number of boats needed is 6. Students may also say $4 \times 6 = 24$. By any of these methods, we find that all the campers can go boating, but not all the boats will be filled.

- Assign homework **Questions 7–16** after Part 2. In homework **Question 13,** $71 \div 3 = 23$ R2. This tells us that we need 24 seats. 23 seats are full (3 people) and one seat has two people (the remainder). In **Question 14,** the solution 13 R1 means there will be 13 students in 4 of the groups and one group will have 14 students. In **Question 15,** since $82 \div 6 = 13$ R4, Jacob needs 14 pages. He will have 13 full pages and 4 pictures on the 14th page.

- DPP items G and I review skills that will be helpful for students when they analyze data for the *TV Survey* in Lesson 1. DPP Task J provides practice using base-ten shorthand to model division. Task L reviews fraction concepts.

- Remind students to prepare for the quiz on facts related to the last six facts by practicing with their *Triangle Flash Cards.*

- Assign Home Practice Parts 5 and 6 in the *Discovery Assignment Book* for practice with fractions and problem solving.

Answers for Parts 5 and 6 of the Home Practice may be found in the Answer Key at the end of this lesson and at the end of this unit.

Assessment

Ask students to model 49 divided by 3 using base-ten pieces or base-ten shorthand. Then, ask them to compute using the forgiving method or another paper-and-pencil method. Record students' abilities to model division using base-ten pieces on the *Observational Assessment Record*.

Name _____ Date _____

Part 5 Create a Fraction

You may use your own fraction chart or the Fraction Chart in the *Student Guide* in Unit 12 Lesson 3 to help you solve these problems.

A. Write a fraction that is larger than $\frac{1}{2}$, but smaller than $\frac{3}{4}$. _____

B. Write a fraction that is a little bit smaller than $\frac{1}{8}$. _____

C. Write a fraction that is double $\frac{1}{10}$. _____

D. Write a fraction that is much larger than $\frac{1}{3}$, but smaller than $\frac{11}{12}$. _____

Part 6 Prizes

The children's hospital plans to spend $100 on 100 stuffed animals for prizes for a raffle. The tiny ones are 10¢, the medium ones cost $2.00, and the large ones cost $5. They will buy some of each kind. (There are many solutions to this problem. If you need more work space, use a separate sheet of paper.)

1. How many of each can they buy?

2. What strategy or strategies did you use to solve this problem?

3. How did you check your answer to see if it was correct?

4. Show another solution to this problem.

Discovery Assignment Book - Page 215

---

2. Some of the campers want to go boating. Each boat can safely hold 4 people. There are 6 boats and 22 campers.
   A. Can they all go boating?
   B. Will all the boats be full?

Write a story for each of the following problems. Then, solve the problems. You may show your work using base-ten shorthand. Remember to talk about any remainder.

3. $34 \div 7$ 4. $81 \div 3$

5. $67 \div 6$ 6. $75 \div 4$

Use the forgiving method to solve the following division problems. Remember to record your final answer, the quotient, and the remainder. Estimate to make sure your answer is reasonable.

7. $74 \div 2$ 8. $87 \div 3$

9. $43 \div 3$ 10. $95 \div 8$

11. $73 \div 6$ 12. $97 \div 4$

13. A. The fourth-grade students at Bessie Coleman School are going on a field trip to the museum. There are 66 students and 5 adults who will be riding the bus. Each seat on the bus will hold 3 people. Use the forgiving method or mental math to divide 71 by 3. What remainder do you get?
   B. What does this remainder mean?
   C. How many seats will the bus need to have?

Student Guide - Page 369

---

14. A. Once the students arrive at the museum, each adult will take a group of students to see the exhibits. Use the forgiving method or mental math to divide 66 by 5. What remainder do you get?
   B. What does the remainder mean?
   C. Show how you can divide the 66 students into 5 groups.

15. A. Jacob took pictures while at the museum. He was going to put them into a photograph album. He has 82 pictures. Each page of his album will hold 6 pictures. How many full pages will he have?
   B. Will there be any remaining pictures?

16. The museum runs a train through several exhibits. Each car holds 6 people. The train has 9 cars.
   A. Can the whole group (students and adults) ride the train at the same time?
   B. How many cars will be needed in all?

Student Guide - Page 370

AT A GLANCE

Math Facts and Daily Practice and Problems

DPP Bit G develops number sense. Items H and K practice multiplication and division facts. Bit I reviews finding median and mean. Task J asks students to represent division with base-ten shorthand. Task L reviews fraction concepts.

Part 1. Modeling Division

1. Discuss how to divide 57 marbles between 2 children.
2. Students estimate the number of marbles each child will get.
3. Model dividing 57 by 2 using base-ten pieces along with the students.
4. Discuss the remainder of dividing 57 by 2.
5. Students practice modeling division problems using base-ten pieces.
6. Discuss division symbols.
7. Students write stories for division sentences.
8. Students complete the Modeling Division section *(Questions 1–6)* in the *Student Guide.*

Part 2. The Forgiving Method

1. Discuss the forgiving method as a paper-and-pencil method for division.
2. Do several division problems using the forgiving method with one-digit divisors and two-digit dividends.
3. Students complete the forgiving method section *(Questions 7–14)* Activity Pages in the *Student Guide.* Remind students to estimate.

Homework

1. Assign homework *Questions 1–6* after Part 1 and discuss them with the class.
2. Assign homework *Questions 7–16* after Part 2.
3. Assign Home Practice Parts 5 and 6.
4. Students continue to practice division facts using the *Triangle Flash Cards: Last Six Facts.*

Assessment

Ask students to model 49 divided by 3 using base-ten pieces and then compute the quotient using paper and pencil. Record students' abilities on the *Observational Assessment Record.*

Notes:

Student Guide

Questions 1–14 (SG pp. 364–368)

1. No, because 2 does not divide 75 evenly.

2. Answers will vary. Since $80 \div 2 = 40$, about (but less than) 40 marbles each.

3. Ana and Roberto can pass out the marbles fairly or they can divide 75 by 2 and then distribute the marbles based on their answer.

4. 30 marbles

5. Answers will vary. A possible response: Ana and her friends have 78 marbles to share among the 6 children. Each person would get 13 marbles.

6. Answers will vary. A possible response: There are 93 marbles to be divided among 4 children. Each child will get 23 marbles. There will be 1 marble left over.

7. Answers will vary. Possible guesses include 10 or 15 marbles.

8. She needs 40 marbles to give 20 marbles to each child. Since she only has 35 marbles left, she knows that giving 20 marbles to each child is too much.

9. **A.** More than 10, but less than 20 and 15.

   B. *13 R4

   C. The quotient means they need at least 13 cabins.

   D. *The remainder means they need 14 cabins so that all boys will have a place to sleep.

   E. *1 possible arrangement: 13 cabins with 7 boys and 1 cabin with 4 boys.

   F. *2 other possible arrangements: 11 cabins with 7 boys and 3 cabins with 6 boys or 12 cabins with 7 boys, 1 cabin with 6 boys, and 1 cabin with 5 boys.

10. **A.** About 5 boys

    B. *$43 \div 9 = 4$ R7. One possible answer: 7 tents will have 5 boys and 2 tents will have 4 boys.

11. 16 R1

12. 23

13. 8

14. 14 R5

Homework (SG pp. 368–370)

Questions 1–16

1. *5 tents, with 2 poles left over

2. **A.** *Yes. One possible solution:

   Boat 1 · · · ·   · · · · Boat 4

   Boat 2 · · · ·   · · · · Boat 5

   Boat 3 · · · ·   · · Boat 6

   B. *No.

   Note: Stories will vary for *Questions 3–6.*

3. 4 R6

4. 27

5. 11 R1

6. 18 R3

7. 37

8. 29

9. 14 R1

10. 11 R7

11. 12 R1

12. 24 R1

13. **A.** *23 R2 One possible solution:

    B. *The remainder means that one more seat is needed for the remaining 2 people.

    C. *24

---

*Answers and/or discussion are included in the Lesson Guide.

**Answers for all the Home Practice in the *Discovery Assignment Book* are at the end of the unit.

14. **A.** *13 R1

 B. *The remainder means 66 students cannot be divided evenly into 5 groups. There will be one student left over.

 C. *There will be 4 groups with 13 students and one group with 14 students.

15. **A.** 13 full pages

 B. Yes. 4 remaining pictures.

16. **A.** No.

 B. 12 cars

Discovery Assignment Book

**Home Practice (DAB p. 215)

Part 5. Create a Fraction

Questions A–D

Answers will vary. Possible responses:

 A. $\frac{2}{3}$

 B. $\frac{1}{10}$

 C. $\frac{1}{5}$ or $\frac{2}{10}$

 D. $\frac{10}{12}$

Part 6. Prizes

Questions 1–4

1. Answers will vary. Possible solution: 16 large, 8 medium, 40 tiny stuffed animals

2. Answers will vary.

3. $16 \times \$5 + 8 \times \$2 + 40 \times \$.10 = \$100$

4. Another possible solution: 15 large, 10 medium, 50 tiny stuffed animals

*Answers and/or discussion are included in the Lesson Guide.

**Answers for all the Home Practice in the *Discovery Assignment Book* are at the end of the unit.

LESSON GUIDE

More Division

 Children expand their understanding of division by modeling problems using the base-ten pieces and using the forgiving method. This lesson emphasizes three- and four-digit dividends. Using good estimates and interpreting remainders are stressed.

Key Content

- Representing division using base-ten pieces.
- Dividing with one-digit divisors and three- and four-digit dividends using paper and pencil.
- Estimating quotients.
- Interpreting remainders.

Daily Practice and Problems: Bits for Lesson 3

M. TV Survey (URG p. 18)

Use paper and pencil or mental math to solve the following problems.

1. According to a recent study, the average American eighth-grader spends about 4 hours a day watching TV. How many hours in a year will an eighth-grader spend watching TV?

2. A school year is approximately 180 days long. How many hours is a student in school, if a school day is 6 hours long?

O. TV Survey Graph (URG p. 19)

1. How many students watched between 2 and 3 hours of TV?

2. How many students are included in this data?

3. How many students watched 4 hours or more?

4. How many watched less than 2 hours?

5. What is the most common number of hours watched?

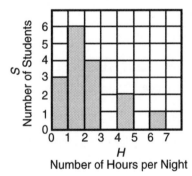

Number of Hours per Night

Q. Division Practice (URG p. 20)

A. $60 \div 8 =$

B. $25 \div 4 =$

C. $35 \div 8 =$

D. $50 \div 6 =$

E. $30 \div 7 =$

F. $45 \div 6 =$

DPP Tasks are on page 60. Suggestions for using the DPPs are on page 60.

Materials List

Print Materials for Students

	Math Facts and Daily Practice and Problems	Activity	Homework	Written Assessment
Student Books				
Student Guide		*More Division* Pages 371–372	*More Division* Homework Section Pages 372–373	
Discovery Assignment Book		*Division Dot-to-Dot* Page 223	Home Practice Part 3 Page 214	Home Practice Part 4 Page 214
Teacher Resources				
Facts Resource Guide ⊙	DPP Item 13Q			
Unit Resource Guide	DPP Items M–R Pages 18–20 ⊙			

⊙ *available on Teacher Resource CD*

All Transparency Masters, Blackline Masters, and Assessment Blackline Masters in the Unit Resource Guide are on the Teacher Resource CD.

Supplies for Each Student Group

set of base-ten pieces: 2 packs, 14 flats, 30 skinnies, 50 bits

Materials for the Teacher

Observational Assessment Record (Unit Resource Guide, Pages 7–8 and Teacher Resource CD)
overhead base-ten pieces, optional

Developing the Activity

The TIMS Candy Company sells candy to a local grocery chain. If the chain requests Chocos, the candy is divided equally among the stores in the chain.

Ask students to model the following problem using base-ten pieces:

- *Mrs. Haddad had 547 Chocos to sell. If a grocery chain has 4 stores, how much candy will each store get?*

- *Make an estimate. Will more than 100 Chocos be shipped to each store? How do you know?*

Children should model the 547 Chocos with base-ten pieces using the Fewest Pieces Rule as shown in Figure 9.

Figure 9: *Representing 547 Chocos*

Since there are 5 flats, each of which represents 100, students should readily see that each store will get more than 100 Chocos. To develop estimation skills, ask:

- *Will the amount be over 200 Chocos?*

- *Will the amount be closer to 100 or 200?* (100)

To help students visualize the division, have them use paper squares labeled Store 1, Store 2, etc. Ask children to model distributing the Chocos among the 4 stores. One way is first to distribute a flat (100 chocos) to each. This leaves 1 flat, 4 skinnies, and 7 bits (147 chocos) as shown in Figure 10.

The remaining flat now must be broken into 10 skinnies so that there are now 14 skinnies. Each store gets 3 skinnies (or 30 Chocos) as shown in Figure 11.

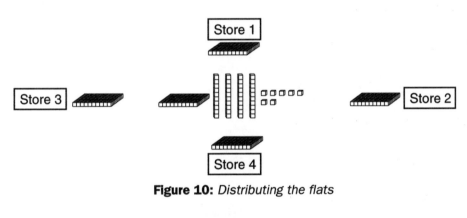

Figure 10: *Distributing the flats*

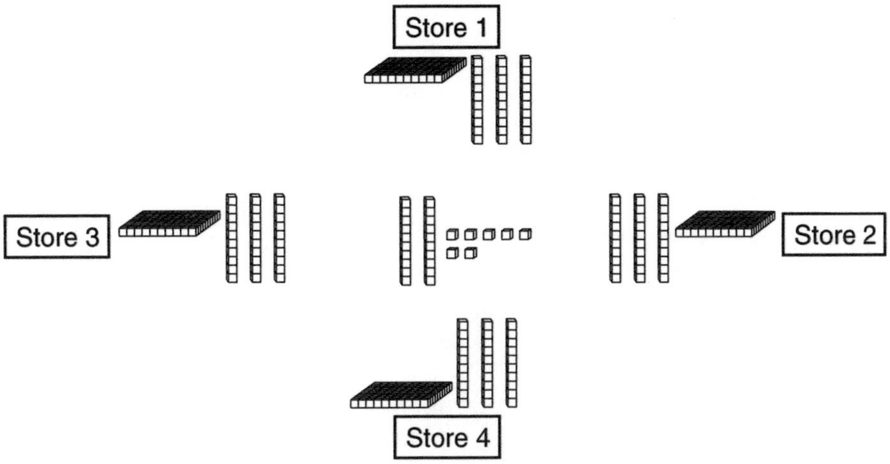

Figure 11: *Distributing the skinnies*

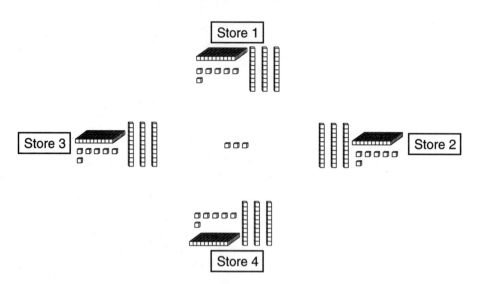

Figure 12: *Distributing the bits*

TIMS Tip

Throughout class discussion, ask students about the amounts represented by the base-ten pieces. For example, 1 flat, 4 skinnies, and 7 bits represents 1 hundred, 4 tens, and 7 ones, or 147.

The remaining 2 skinnies can be broken up into 20 bits so that there are 27 bits. Each store receives 6 bits (6 Chocos) with 3 bits remaining.

Thus, each store receives 136 Chocos, with 3 Chocos remaining as shown in Figure 12.

Do several more problems in the context of the candy factory, modeling the problem with the base-ten pieces. Use these problems as examples:

- $427 \div 3$
- $572 \div 7$
- $205 \div 5$
- *How can you compute the last problem using mental math?* ($200 \div 5 = 40$ and $5 \div 5 = 1$, so $205 \div 5 = 41$.)

When students are ready to move from the base-ten pieces to symbols, go through a problem using the forgiving method. It often helps children to make good estimates when they visualize the dividend in terms of the base-ten pieces.

Using the first Chocos problem, $547 \div 4$, a first estimate might be 100. Show children how to record this:

$$\begin{array}{r} 4 \overline{)\ 547} \\ -400 \quad 100 \\ \hline 147 \end{array}$$

Make sure they understand that the 100 is the number of Chocos each store receives. In terms of base-ten pieces, each store receives a flat. The 400 represents the number of Chocos being shipped and the 147 is the number of Chocos that still need to be taken care of or distributed.

The next guess may not be so easy. Help children think about good estimates. We know 100 is way too large. Half of 100 gives a product of 200 (50 × 4). Thus, the number must be less than 50. Some children may guess low, for example, 10. This is fine. The method still works, but will take more steps. The only time we need to erase when using the forgiving method is when we guess too high. For example, a reasonable guess which is too high is 40:

$$
\begin{array}{r}
4\ )\ \overline{547} \\
-\ 400\ \ |\ \ 100 \\
\hline
147 \\
-\ 160\ \ |\ \ 40 \\
\end{array}
$$

If we have only 147 Chocos, we can not ship 160, so this estimate is too high. A child may then erase 160 and try 30.

$$
\begin{array}{r}
4\ )\ \overline{547} \\
-\ 400\ \ |\ \ 100 \\
\hline
147 \\
-\ 120\ \ |\ \ 30 \\
\hline
27 \\
\end{array}
$$

Then 4 divides 27, 6 times with 3 left over. The finished problem should look like:

$$
\begin{array}{r}
136\ R3 \\
4\ )\ \overline{547} \\
-\ 400\ \ |\ \ 100 \\
\hline
147 \\
-\ 120\ \ |\ \ 30 \\
\hline
27 \\
-\ 24\ \ |\ \ 6 \\
\hline
3 \\
\end{array}
$$

Practice several more problems, including problems with 4-digit dividends. Make sure students estimate the quotient first. They can also make up stories for the problems and interpret the quotients and remainders. Possible examples include:

- 512 ÷ 6
- 740 ÷ 8
- 3227 ÷ 4
- 809 ÷ 3
- 1560 ÷ 4

Students complete the *More Division* Activity Pages in the *Student Guide*. Discuss the problems together, especially focusing on the meaning of the remainder. There are enough problems provided for several nights of homework to be discussed in class the next day.

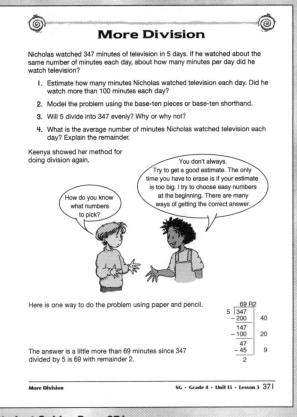

More Division

Nicholas watched 347 minutes of television in 5 days. If he watched about the same number of minutes each day, about how many minutes per day did he watch television?

1. Estimate how many minutes Nicholas watched television each day. Did he watch more than 100 minutes each day?

2. Model the problem using the base-ten pieces or base-ten shorthand.

3. Will 5 divide into 347 evenly? Why or why not?

4. What is the average number of minutes Nicholas watched television each day? Explain the remainder.

Keenya showed her method for doing division again.

How do you know what numbers to pick?

You don't always. Try to get a good estimate. The only time you have to erase is if your estimate is too big. I try to choose easy numbers at the beginning. There are many ways of getting the correct answer.

Here is one way to do the problem using paper and pencil.

$$
\begin{array}{r}
69\ R2 \\
5\ )\ \overline{347} \\
-\ 200\ \ |\ \ 40 \\
\hline
147 \\
-\ 100\ \ |\ \ 20 \\
\hline
47 \\
-\ 45\ \ |\ \ 9 \\
\hline
2 \\
\end{array}
$$

The answer is a little more than 69 minutes since 347 divided by 5 is 69 with remainder 2.

More Division   SG · Grade 4 · Unit 13 · Lesson 3 371

***Student Guide* - Page 371**

Daily Practice and Problems: Tasks for Lesson 3

N. Task: Building with Cubes
(URG p. 18)

1. Roberto made a building out of 168 connecting cubes. Each floor contains 6 cubes. How many floors are in the building?

2. Shannon has 126 cubes. The building she creates has 9 floors. Each floor has the same number of cubes. How many cubes are in each floor of Shannon's building?

3. Nila has $\frac{1}{2}$ of the number of cubes as Roberto. Nila's building has 7 floors. If each floor has the same number of cubes, how many cubes are in each floor of Nila's building?

P. Task: Writing Division Stories
(URG p. 19)

Write a story for 256 ÷ 7. Remember to talk about the remainder. Then, find the answer. You may use base-ten shorthand or another paper-and-pencil method to solve the problem.

R. Task: Paper-and-Pencil Division
(URG p. 20)

Describe how you can decide which of the problems below will have a remainder and which will come out even. Then, solve the problems using paper and pencil. Check your answers using multiplication.

1. 87 ÷ 3
2. 178 ÷ 2
3. 577 ÷ 6

Suggestions for Teaching the Lesson

Math Facts

DPP Bit Q provides division practice with remainders using the last six facts.

Homework and Practice

- Homework is provided in the *Student Guide*. Distribute the problems over several nights and discuss the problems the next day. It is better for students to do a few problems carefully and explain their work than do many problems carelessly.

- The *Division Dot-to-Dot* Activity Page in the *Discovery Assignment Book* can also be assigned as homework.

- DPP Tasks N, P, and R provide division practice in various contexts.

- DPP Bits M and O review multiplication and graphing skills needed to analyze the *TV Survey* data for Lesson 1.

- Part 3 of the Home Practice in the *Discovery Assignment Book* provides computation practice with multiplication and division.

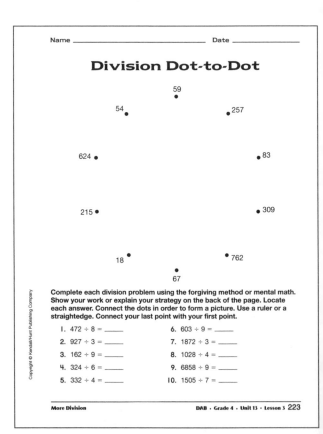

Discovery Assignment Book - Page 223

Assessment

- Document students' abilities to represent division using base-ten pieces on the *Observational Assessment Record*.
- Use Home Practice Part 4 as an assessment of students' division skills.

Answers for Parts 3 and 4 of the Home Practice can be found in the Answer Key at the end of this lesson and at the end of this unit.

Name _____ Date _____

Part 3 Multiplication and Division Practice

Use paper and pencil or mental math to solve the following problems. If you need more work space to show your work, you may use a separate sheet of paper. Estimate to make sure your answers are reasonable.

1. A. 267 × 7 =   B. 78 × 23 =   C. 30 × 58 =   D. 73 × 400 =

E. 6004 × 8 =   F. 269 ÷ 3 =   G. 379 ÷ 2 =   H. 467 ÷ 8 =

2. Explain your estimation strategy for Question 1A.

Part 4 More Division Practice

Use paper and pencil or mental math to solve the following problems. Estimate to be sure your answers are reasonable.

A. 3606 ÷ 6 =   B. 4587 ÷ 7 =   C. 6675 ÷ 5 =   D. 855 ÷ 9 =

DIVISION

Discovery Assignment Book - Page 214

---

5. Mr. Haddad of the TIMS Candy Company has 398 Chocos to divide evenly among 6 orders.
    A. Estimate the number of Chocos each order will receive.
    B. Model the problem using base-ten shorthand.
    C. How many Chocos will be in each order?
    D. How many Chocos will be left?
    E. Do the problem using the forgiving method.

6. Joe made 282 Chocos. Mrs. Haddad had to divide them among 5 orders.
    A. Estimate the number of Chocos each order will receive.
    B. Model the problem using base-ten shorthand.
    C. How many Chocos will be in each order?
    D. How many Chocos will be left?
    E. Do the problem using the forgiving method.

7. One of the stores decided to sell Chocos in small bags. Each bag will have 6 Chocos in it. Mrs. Haddad has 96 Chocos. How many bags will she use?
    A. Model the problem using base-ten shorthand.
    B. How many bags will she use?
    C. Do the problem using the forgiving method.

Homework

Model each of the following problems in Questions 1–4 with base-ten shorthand. Then, solve them using the forgiving method.

1. 643 ÷ 5   2. 852 ÷ 3   3. 1533 ÷ 8   4. 2835 ÷ 9

Solve the problems in Questions 5–8 using mental math or pencil and paper.

5. 9076 ÷ 7   6. 2412 ÷ 3   7. 1889 ÷ 2   8. 3600 ÷ 4

More Division

Student Guide - Page 372

Solve the following problems using paper-and-pencil methods or mental math. Remember to record your final answer. Also, if there is a remainder, remember to describe how it is used in each problem.

9. Mr. Haddad's company packages damaged Chocos in packages called "Handful Packs." At the end of the day, Carmen, an employee who packages candy, has been given 132 damaged pieces of candy. How many Handful Packs can Carmen make if each pack must contain 8 Chocos?

10. The TIMS Candy Company has 176 employees. Mr. Haddad evenly divides his staff into four categories: management, candy making, packaging, and distribution. How many employees are in each category?

11. A. Hank works 5 hours a day. He gets paid $7 an hour. How much does Hank earn in one work week (5 days)?
    B. How much does he earn in four weeks?

12. James's candy-wrapping machine grabs 6 Chocos at a time and wraps them in about 1 second. James is helping to fill an order for 4568 Chocos.
    A. How many times must the candy-wrapping machine run in order to wrap the Chocos individually?
    B. Will it take more or less time than 30 minutes to wrap all of these candies? How did you decide?

13. The TIMS Candy Company holds an annual company picnic. One hundred eighteen employees came to the picnic. Sixty-seven employees brought one guest. Forty-three employees brought two guests. The rest of the employees brought three guests. How many people attended the picnic in all?

14. Bob transports boxes of nuts for the Crunchy Nut factory. Nine individual boxes of Crunchy Nuts fit inside a carton. How many cartons will Bob need to deliver 3100 boxes of Crunchy Nuts to Bessie Coleman School for their fund-raiser?

15. A. If 7 classrooms divide the 3100 boxes of Crunchy Nuts evenly for the fund-raiser, how many boxes should each classroom get?
    B. Mrs. Randall's classroom has 32 students. If each child sells about 14 boxes of Crunchy Nuts, will they sell all the boxes of Crunchy Nuts Mrs. Randall's class needs to sell?

16. In the end, Mrs. Randall's class raised $1835. How many boxes did Mrs. Randall's class sell, if each box cost $5?

Student Guide - Page 373

AT A GLANCE

Math Facts and Daily Practice and Problems

DPP Bit M reviews multiplication skills. Tasks N, P, and R practice division skills. Bit O reviews analyzing a graph. Bit Q provides division facts practice.

Developing the Activity

1. Discuss representing 547 ÷ 4 using base-ten pieces and ask students to model other examples.
2. Compute 547 ÷ 4 using the forgiving method.
3. Students model and compute several more problems with three- and four-digit dividends.
4. Students complete the *More Division* Activity Pages in the *Student Guide.*

Homework

1. Assign the homework questions in the *Student Guide* over several nights.
2. Assign the *Division Dot-to-Dot* Activity Page in the *Discovery Assignment Book.*
3. Assign Home Practice Part 3.

Assessment

1. Record students' abilities to model division using base-ten pieces on the *Observational Assessment Record.*
2. Use Home Practice Part 4 as an assessment.

Notes:

Student Guide

Questions 1–7 (SG pp. 371–372)

1. No, one possible estimate:
   $350 \div 5 = 70$ min.

2. One possible solution:

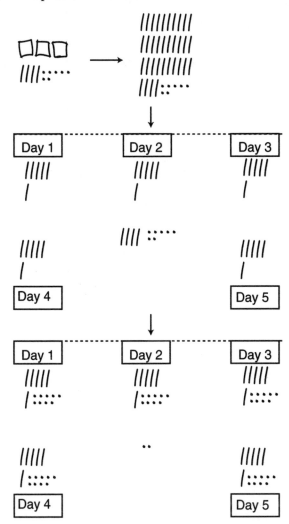

3. No, because 347 is not a multiple of 5.

4. 69 R2; Possible response: 5 will not divide evenly into 347, so Nicholas could not have watched exactly the same amount of TV each day. To the nearest minute, Nicholas watched an average of 69 minutes each day. To the nearest 10 minutes, he watched an average of 70 minutes each day.

5. **A.** One possible estimate: Less than 70 Chocos

   B.

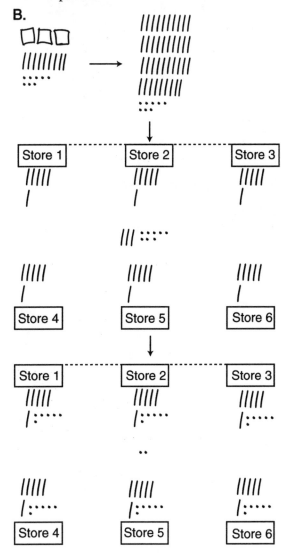

   C. 66 Chocos

   D. 2 Chocos

   E. Steps will vary. 66 R2

6. **A.** One possible estimate: $300 \div 5 = 60$ Chocos

   B. Shorthand steps will vary.

   C. 56 Chocos

   D. 2 Chocos

   E. Steps will vary. 56 R2

*Answers and/or discussion are included in the Lesson Guide.

**Answers for all the Home Practice in the *Discovery Assignment Book* are at the end of the unit.

7. A.

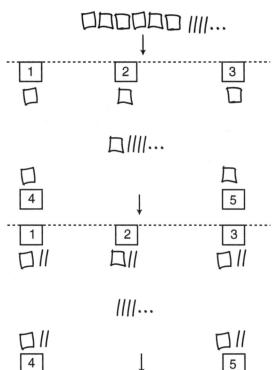

One possible solution is:

```
      128 R3
 5 )643
   -500 |100
    143
   -100 | 20
     43
    -40 |  8
      3
```

B. 16

C. Steps will vary. 16

Homework (SG pp. 372–373)

Questions 1–16

1. 128 R3; One possible shorthand model is:

2. 284; Shorthand models will vary.

One possible solution is:

```
      284
 3 )852
   -600 |200
    252
   -240 | 80
     12
    -12 |  4
      0
```

3. 191 R5; Shorthand models will vary.

One possible solution is:

```
       191 R5
 8 )1533
   -800 |100
    733
   -720 | 90
     13
    -8  |  1
      5
```

4. 315; Shorthand models will vary.

One possible solution is:

```
       315
 9 )2835
  -2700 |300
    135
   -90  | 10
     45
   -45  |  5
      0
```

*Answers and/or discussion are included in the Lesson Guide.

Answers for all the Home Practice in the *Discovery Assignment Book* are at the end of the unit.

5. 1296 R4; Methods will vary.
One possible solution is:

```
        1296 R4
    7)9076
     - 7000   1000
       2076
     - 1400    200
        676
      - 630     90
         46
       - 42      6
          4
```

6. 804; Methods will vary. 2400 ÷ 3 = 800;
12 ÷ 3 = 4; 800 + 4 = 804

7. 944 R1; Methods will vary.
One possible solution is:

```
        944 R1
    2)1889
     - 1800    900
         89
       - 80     40
          9
        - 8      4
          1
```

8. 900; Methods will vary.

9. 16 Handful Paks. There will be 4 candies
left over.

10. 44 employees

11. **A.** $175

   B. $700

12. **A.** 761 R2; To wrap all the candies the
machine must run 762 times.

   B. Less than 30 minutes. Possible strategy:
Since 30 × 60 = 1800 sec,
30 min = 1800 sec. The machine needs to
run for 762 sec which is less than 30 min.

13. 67 × 2 + 43 × 3 + 8 × 4 = 295 people

14. 345 cartons

15. **A.** 3100 ÷ 7 = 442 R6. 6 classrooms receive
443 boxes and 1 classroom receives
442 boxes.

   B. Yes. 32 × 14 = 448 boxes. 448 > 443.

16. 367 boxes

Discovery Assignment Book

**Home Practice (DAB p. 214)

Part 3. Multiplication and Division Practice

Questions 1–2

   1. **A.** 1869

      B. 1794

      C. 1740

      D. 29,200

      E. 48,032

      F. 89 R2

      G. 189 R1

      H. 58 R3

   2. Possible strategy: Skip count by 250 seven
times—250, 500, 750, 1000, 1250, 1500, 1750.

Part 4. More Division Practice

Questions A–D

   A. 601

   B. 655 R2

   C. 1335

   D. 95

Division Dot-to-Dot (DAB p. 223)

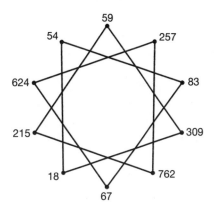

1.	59	6.	67
2.	309	7.	624
3.	18	8.	257
4.	54	9.	762
5.	83	10.	215

*Answers and/or discussion are included in the Lesson Guide.

**Answers for all the Home Practice in the *Discovery Assignment Book* are at the end of the unit.

LESSON GUIDE 4

Solving Problems Using Multiplication and Division

Estimated Class Sessions: 2

Using the context of the *TV Survey* students completed in Lesson 1, students solve problems involving multiplication and division. They practice choosing appropriate tools and methods of computation as well as applying paper-and-pencil methods in problem-solving situations. Students also explore division with zero using what they know about fact families.

Key Content

- Solving problems involving multiplication and division.
- Choosing appropriate methods of computation.
- Dividing with zero.

Key Vocabulary

unique solution

Curriculum Sequence

Before This Unit

Operations with Zero. In the Adventure Book story *Cipher Force* in Grade 3 Unit 11, students explored using zeros in addition, subtraction, multiplication, and division. In Grade 4 Unit 3 Lesson 1 students discussed multiplying by zero and one.

Materials List

Print Materials for Students

	Math Facts and Daily Practice and Problems	Activity	Homework	Written Assessment
Student Books				
Student Guide		Solving Problems Using Multiplication and Division Pages 374–376	Solving Problems Using Multiplication and Division Homework Section Pages 377–378	
Discovery Assignment Book			Home Practice Part 7 Page 216	
Teacher Resources				
Facts Resource Guide	DPP Items 13S & 13U			DPP Item 13S *Facts Quiz: Last Six Facts*
Unit Resource Guide	DPP Items S–V Pages 21–22			DPP Item S *Facts Quiz: Last Six Facts* Page 21 and *Unit 13 Quiz* Page 72
Generic Section		Small Multiplication Tables, 1 per 4 students		

available on Teacher Resource CD

All Transparency Masters, Blackline Masters, and Assessment Blackline Masters in the Unit Resource Guide are on the Teacher Resource CD.

Supplies for Each Student

calculator

Materials for the Teacher

Observational Assessment Record (Unit Resource Guide, Pages 7–8 and Teacher Resource CD)
Individual Assessment Record Sheet (Teacher Implementation Guide, Assessment section and
   Teacher Resource CD)

Student Guide - Page 374

Content Note

Division and Zero. To solve $0 \div 4 = n$, we must find a
number n that makes $4 \times n = 0$ true. Since $4 \times 0 = 0$,
then $n = 0$ and $0 \div 4 = 0$. In fact, since any number times
zero is zero, zero divided by any number (other than zero)
is zero.

To solve $4 \div 0 = n$, we must find a number n that makes
$n \times 0 = 4$ a true statement. Since any number times zero
is zero, there is no number for n that will make the statement true. So, we say that division by zero is undefined.

Consider $0 \div 0 = n$. What number n will make the statement
$n \times 0 = 0$ true? $1 \times 0 = 0$, $2 \times 0 = 0$, $3 \times 0 = 0$, and so
on. In fact, any number will make the statement true. Since
there is no unique solution to $0 \div 0 = n$, we say that $0 \div 0$
is undefined.

Developing the Activity

Part 1. Word Problems

Questions 1–3 provide practice using mental math
and paper-and-pencil methods to multiply and divide.
To complete *Questions 4–7* students must choose an
appropriate method of computation for solving the
problem. They choose whether to find an estimate
or an exact answer and whether to use mental math,
paper and pencil, or a calculator. Different students
may choose different methods. For example, to answer
Question 4, student must find the average number of
minutes a student reads each night. To find the mean,
students may either choose to use a calculator, paper
and pencil, or a combination of the two methods.

Part 2. Zeros and Division

Use the following discussion prompts to guide a
discussion about division and zero. First, review
the inverse relationship between multiplication and
division using fact families. Ask:

- *Write the four sentences in the fact family for*
  $12 \div 4$. ($12 \div 4 = 3$, $12 \div 3 = 4$, $3 \times 4 = 12$,
  $4 \times 3 = 12$)

Remind students that there is only one answer to a
division problem. Each division problem has a
unique solution. That is, there is only one number
that makes the following statement true:

- $12 \div 4 = ?$, since $4 \times ? = 12$.

- *What number makes the above statement true?* (3)

- *For each statement, find one number that makes*
  the statement true.

   $10 \div 5 = ?$, since $5 \times ? = 10$ (2)

   $18 \div 3 = ?$, since $3 \times ? = 18$ (6)

   $8 \div 1 = ?$, since $1 \times ? = 8$ (8)

   $0 \div 2 = ?$, since $2 \times ? = 0$ (0)

   $0 \div 3 = ?$, since $3 \times ? = 0$ (0)

   $0 \div 10 = ?$, since $10 \times ? = 0$ (0)

- *Find $0 \div 9 = ?$ Justify your solution.* ($0 \div 9 = 0$,
  since $9 \times 0 = 0$)

Use the same reasoning to explore division by zero.

- *Find one number that makes the statement true:*

   $2 \div 0 = ?$, since $0 \times ? = 2$

Students should see that since zero times any number
is zero, there is no number that will makes the statement true. We say that division by zero is **undefined.**

What happens when we try to divide zero by zero?

- *Find one number that makes the statement true:*

$$0 \div 0 = ?, \text{ since } 0 \times ? = 0$$

Students may say that $0 \times 1 = 0$, $0 \times 2 = 0$, $0 \times 3 = 0$. In fact zero times any number is zero. So, there is not just one number that makes the statement true. There is not a unique solution, so we say that $0 \div 0$ is undefined as well.

The Zeros and Division section in the *Student Guide* reinforces the concepts explored above. Students can read and answer *Questions 8–13* together in pairs or small groups. Note that *Question 13* asks students to enter division by zero problems on a calculator. Calculators will display an error message if asked to divide by zero.

Suggestions for Teaching the Lesson

Math Facts

DPP Bit U reviews division problems with zero and one.

Homework and Practice

- Assign the problems in the Homework section of the *Student Guide*.
- DPP Task T provides practice with multiplication and division through a word problem involving money.
- Home Practice Part 7 is a set of word problems.

Answers for Part 7 of the Home Practice can be found in the Answer Key at the end of this lesson and at the end of this unit.

Assessment

- Use the *Unit 13 Quiz* Assessment Blackline Master to assess students' skills in multiplying and dividing whole numbers.
- Use DPP Bit S to assess students' fluency with the 12 division facts related to the last six multiplication facts.
- Use the *Observational Assessment Record* to document students' progress solving problems using multiplication and division. Transfer information from the Unit 13 *Observational Assessment Record* to students' *Individual Assessment Record Sheets*.

---

5. Using the class data they found that, on average, a student in Mrs. Dewey's class reads 45 minutes for pleasure each evening.
   A. On average, how many minutes does a student in Mrs. Dewey's class read in four days?
   B. How many hours?

6. A. On average, how many minutes does a student in Mrs. Dewey's class read in 10 days?
   B. How many minutes in 30 days?
   C. How many in 100 days?

7. A. On average, about how many minutes does a student in Mrs. Dewey's class read for pleasure in one year?
   B. About how many hours?
   C. Is the amount of time a student in Mrs. Dewey's class reads for pleasure in one year more or less than the number of hours in a month? (*Hint:* See Question 2A.)

Zeros and Division

Tanya and Frank were studying their division facts. They began with $24 \div 4$.

Frank wrote, "$24 \div 4 = 7$."

Tanya wrote, "$24 \div 4 = 6$."

She said, "One of us must be wrong. There can't be two different answers to the same division problem."

Mrs. Dewey said, "That's right, Tanya. Each division problem has a unique solution. Work together to find the correct answer. Try using fact families."

8. Write the fact family for $24 \div 4$. Who is correct, Tanya or Frank?

Tanya said, "To find the answer to $24 \div 4$, I look for the only number that makes $4 \times ? = 24$ true. Since $4 \times 6 = 24$, then $24 \div 4 = 6$."

"That's good thinking," said Mrs. Dewey. "Let's use your reasoning to think about division and zero. Find $0 \div 24$."

Tanya replied, "To find $0 \div 24$, I find the only number that makes $24 \times ? = 0$ true. Since any number times zero is zero, $24 \times 0 = 0$ and $0 \div 24 = 0$."

9. Use Tanya's reasoning to find $0 \div 5$.

Solving Problems Using Multiplication and Division   SG · Grade 4 · Unit 13 · Lesson 4   375

Student Guide - Page 375

Mrs. Dewey said, "Tanya, now try, $24 \div 0$."

Tanya began, "To find $24 \div 0$, I find the number that makes $0 \times ? = 24$. But, no number makes this number sentence true. What do I do?"

"Since there is no solution for $0 \times ? = 24$, we say that $24 \div 0$ is undefined. In fact, if you use your reasoning with any number divided by zero, you will find the same thing. So, mathematicians say that division by zero is **undefined**."

10. Use Tanya's reasoning to find $5 \div 0$.

"Now, think about $0 \div 0$," said Mrs. Dewey.

This time Frank began, "To think about $0 \div 0$, I try to find the only number that makes $0 \times ? = 0$ true. But, any number works. $0 \times 5 = 0$ and $0 \times 24 = 0$. Zero times any number is zero. Mrs. Dewey, I thought you said there is just one right answer. I remember you said, 'a unique solution.'"

"That's right, Frank," Mrs. Dewey replied. "Since there is not a unique solution, mathematicians say that $0 \div 0$ is undefined as well."

For each statement below, find one number that will make it true. If there is no such number, say so.

11. A. $8 \div 4 = $ _____ , since $4 \times $ _____ $= 8$

    B. $42 \div 7 = $ _____ , since $7 \times $ _____ $= 42$

    C. $5 \div 1 = $ _____ , since $1 \times $ _____ $= 5$

    D. $0 \div 3 = $ _____ , since $3 \times $ _____ $= 0$

    E. $28 \div 7 = $ _____ , since $7 \times $ _____ $= 28$

    F. $2 \div 0 = $ _____ , since $0 \times $ _____ $= 2$

    G. $36 \div 6 = $ _____ , since $6 \times $ _____ $= 36$

    H. $0 \div 0 = $ _____ , since $0 \times $ _____ $= 0$

Solve the following problems. When necessary, use "undefined." Justify your reasoning using related multiplication sentences.

12. A. $35 \div 7 = $ B. $0 \div 7 = $
    C. $7 \div 0 = $ D. $0 \div 0 = $

13. Do the division problems in Question 12 on a calculator. Explain what happens.

376 SG · Grade 4 · Unit 13 · Lesson 4   *Solving Problems Using Multiplication and Division*

Student Guide - Page 376

Homework

A Saturday Visit

Nicholas's cousin Stan came to visit on a Saturday afternoon. Solve the following problems that describe their day.

- Show your calculations using a paper-and-pencil method or explain a mental math strategy.
- Use estimation when appropriate.
- If the answer includes a remainder, explain how the remainder is used.

1. It took Stan 4 hours to get to Nicholas's house. Stan and his mother took the freeway. If Stan's mother drove 55 miles per hour, how many miles away does Stan live?

2. Stan plans to surprise Nicholas with three tickets to see the Silver Blades hockey team. If Stan's dad paid $54 for three tickets, how much did one ticket cost?

3. When Stan arrived, Nicholas was just finishing a book. Nicholas said, "This book has 273 pages. It took me four days to read it." On average, how many pages did Nicholas read each day?

4. A. The boys' mothers talked about their exercise routines while they enjoyed a cup of tea. Stan's mother burns 10 calories in 1 minute on her bike. How many calories does she burn in 20 minutes?

Solving Problems Using Multiplication and Division   SG · Grade 4 · Unit 13 · Lesson 4   377

Student Guide - Page 377

B. Nicholas's mother burns about 9 calories per minute on the Super Step machine. How many calories does she burn in 24 minutes?

C. How many minutes does Nicholas's mother need to use the Super Step machine in order to burn off a 340-calorie dessert?

5. A. When they got back to Nicholas's house, the boys played a board game. While playing, Nicholas had a chance to double his winnings of $2972. How much would Nicholas have if he doubled his money?

B. Instead, Nicholas landed on "Donate your earnings to 4 of your favorite charities." If Nicholas shares his earnings of $2972 equally, how much money will each charity receive?

6. Later in the evening, Nicholas and Stan played a video game involving a skyscraper. In this game you go up 18 floors if you answer all the questions in any one round correctly. If you have a perfect score after 12 rounds, you reach the top of the building. How many stories are in the building in this video game?

7. $1632 \div 8$ 8. $976 \div 4$ 9. $2832 \div 5$

Student Guide - Page 378

Daily Practice and Problems:
Task & Challenge for Lesson 4

T. Task: Saving Quarters
(URG p. 21)

1. The Anderson family saves quarters in a jar. They divide the quarters they save among their four children. If they save 345 quarters, how many quarters does each child receive?

2. How much money does each child receive?

V. Challenge: Even Teams
(URG p. 22)

Nicholas took his cousin Stan to his Wilderness Club picnic. On the way home, Stan and Nicholas wondered how many kids came to the picnic. Nicholas said, "Well, the leaders divided us evenly into 2 groups for the scavenger hunt. For the other games, they divided us evenly into 3 groups, 5 groups, and 6 groups. Finally, when we had the relay races, they divided us evenly into 7 groups." What is the fewest possible number of kids that came to the picnic?

Name_____ Date _____

Part 7   Solving Problems

Choose appropriate methods and tools to solve the following problems. Explain how you solved each problem.

1. Over a four-day period, Frank watched 325 minutes of TV. He watched 60 minutes of TV on Monday, 45 minutes on Tuesday, and 75 minutes on Wednesday.

A. How many minutes did he watch on Thursday?

B. About how many hours of TV did he watch on Thursday?

2. On Monday, Shannon watched 4 times the amount of TV as Luis. If Shannon watched TV for 180 minutes, how many minutes did Luis watch?

3. Mrs. Dewey watched 45 minutes of TV on Monday, 35 minutes on Tuesday, and 1 hour on Wednesday. She did not watch TV on Thursday. What is the mean number of minutes of TV watched by Mrs. Dewey over the four-day period?

4. Mrs. Randall's class watched a total of 5430 minutes of TV over a four-day period.

A. Is this more than less than 50 hours of TV? How do you know?

B. Is this more or less than 100 hours of TV? How do you know?

C. Estimate the number of hours of TV the students in Mrs. Randall's class watched.

5. Mrs. Randall's class decided to change their TV habits. In a follow-up survey, the class watched a total of 3780 minutes of TV in four days.

A. Did they watch more or less TV? How many minutes more or less?

B. As a class, how many hours of TV did they cut out of their daily routine?

Discovery Assignment Book - Page 216

Suggestions for Teaching the Lesson (continued)

Extension

- In this lesson, students calculate the number of hours a child watches TV in a year. They compare this number to the number of hours in a month. Do children watch more or less than a month of TV in a year? To make these calculations, students use the statistic given in the *Student Guide* in Lesson 1: Children between the ages of six and eleven watch an average of three hours of TV each day. Students can make the same calculations using the data collected in *TV Survey*. Students can use their individual data—the average number of hours he or she watched TV in one day (*Question 5* in the *Student Guide* for Lesson 1). They can round this number to the nearest whole hour and make the same calculations as those outlined in *Questions 1–3* of this lesson.
- DPP item V is a challenging word problem that requires an understanding of factors and multiples.

AT A GLANCE

Math Facts and Daily Practice and Problems

DPP item S is a quiz on the 12 division facts related to the last six multiplication facts. Task T is a word problem that practices multiplication and division. Bit U reviews division and zero. Challenge V is a word problem involving factors and multiples.

Part 1. Word Problems

1. Students practice using mental math or paper-and-pencil methods to solve *Questions 1–3* in the *Student Guide.*
2. They choose methods and tools to solve the problems in *Questions 4–7.*

Part 2. Zeros and Division

1. Use the Discussion Prompts in the Lesson Guide to discuss division problems with zeros.
2. Students complete the Zeros and Division section in the *Student Guide.*

Homework

1. Assign the Homework section in the *Student Guide.*
2. Assign Part 7 of the Home Practice.

Assessment

1. Use the *Unit 13 Quiz* Assessment Blackline Master to assess students' multiplication and division skills.
2. Use DPP Bit S to assess students' fluency with the division facts in the Last Six Facts group.
3. Document students' abilities to solve multiplication and division problems on the *Observational Assessment Record.* Transfer appropriate documentation to students' *Individual Assessment Record Sheets.*

Notes:

Unit 13 Quiz

Use paper and pencil to solve the following problems.

1. Solve $894 \div 6$ using any method you wish.

2. A parking garage has 7 floors. For a special concert, workers parked a total of 1278 cars in the garage. If they distributed the cars evenly onto each floor, how many cars did they park on each floor? Explain any remainder.

3. Each of the children in Mr. Harrington's class buys a box of 64 crayons. There are 27 children in the class. How many crayons do the children buy altogether?

4. A parking garage has room for 240 cars on each of the first two floors. The other floors hold 278 cars each. If the total number of floors is 6, how many cars can park in the garage at one time?

Student Guide

Questions 1–13 (SG pp. 374–376)

1. **A.** 30 hours

   B. 90 hours

   C. 300 hours

   D. 1095 hours

2. **A.** 720 hours

   B. More than 1 month; less than 2 months

3. **A.** 167 days; $500 \div 3 = 166$ R2

   B. 24 weeks; $167 \div 7 = 23$ R6

   C. 6 months; $24 \div 4 = 6$ months or
   $167 \div 30 = 5$ R17

4. **A.** 60 minutes

   B. 60 minutes

5. **A.** 180 minutes

   B. 3 hours

6. **A.** 450 minutes

   B. 1350 minutes

   C. 4500 minutes

7. **A.** A possible mental estimate is 16,000 min
   since $300 \times 40 = 12,000$ and
   $400 \times 50 = 20,000$.
   Using a calculator: $365 \times 45 = 16,425$ min.

   B. A possible estimate: $16,000 \div 60$ between
   200 and 300 hours. Using a calculator:
   $16,425 \div 60 = 273.75$ or about 275 hours.

   C. less

8. $24 \div 4 = 6$; $24 \div 6 = 4$; $6 \times 4 = 24$;
   $4 \times 6 = 24$; Tanya

9. $0 \div 5 = 0$, since $5 \times 0 = 0$

10. $5 \div 0$ is undefined, since there is no number
    that makes $0 \times ? = 5$ a true statement.

11. **A.** 2, 2

    B. 6, 6

    C. 5, 5

    D. 0, 0

    E. 4, 4

    F. undefined; No number makes the
    statement true.

    G. 6, 6

    H. undefined; Any number makes the
    statement true, so there is not a
    unique solution.

12. **A.** 5; $35 \div 7 = 5$ since $7 \times 5 = 35$

    B. 0; $0 \div 7 = 0$ since $7 \times 0 = 0$

    C. undefined; $7 \div 0$ is undefined since there
    is no number that makes $0 \times ? = 7$.

    D. $0 \div 0$ is undefined, since there is not just
    one number that makes $0 \times ? = 0$.

13. The calculator computes A ($35 \div 7 = 5$)
    and B ($0 \div 7 = 0$), but gives an error message
    for C ($7 \div 0$) and D ($0 \div 0$), since they
    are undefined.

Homework (SG pp. 377–378)

Questions 1–9

1. 220 miles

2. $18

3. $273 \div 4 = 68$ R1. To the nearest page,
   Nicholas read 68 pages each day.

4. **A.** 200 calories

   B. 216 calories

   C. 38 minutes; $340 \div 9 = 37$ R7

5. **A.** $5944

   B. $743

6. 216 stories

7. 204

8. 244

9. 566 R2

*Answers and/or discussion are included in the Lesson Guide.

**Answers for all the Home Practice in the *Discovery Assignment Book* are at the end of the unit.

Discovery Assignment Book

**Home Practice (DAB p. 216)

Part 7. Solving Problems

Questions 1–5

1. **A.** 145 minutes
   B. About $2\frac{1}{2}$ hrs or between 2 and 3 hrs.

2. 45 minutes

3. 35 minutes

4. **A.** more than;
   50 hrs = 50 × 60 min = 3000 min
   B. less than;
   100 hrs = 100 × 60 min = 6000 min
   C. Answers will vary.
   Possible solution: 5400 ÷ 60 = 90 hrs

5. **A.** less; 1650 minutes less
   B. 27.5 hours

Unit Resource Guide

Unit 13 Quiz (URG p. 72)

Questions 1–4

1. 149

2. 182 cars with 4 extra cars located among the 7 floors.

3. 1728 crayons

4. 1592 cars

*Answers and/or discussion are included in the Lesson Guide.
**Answers for all the Home Practice in the *Discovery Assignment Book* are at the end of the unit.

LESSON GUIDE 5

Plant Growth

Estimated Class Sessions: 2

Students begin a lab designed to show the growth pattern of plants. This lab will be completed in Unit 15. The introductory activity provides students with an opportunity to identify the manipulated, responding, and fixed variables for this experiment. Students will then plant seeds, choose one plant to follow, and take measurements of the plant's growth over time. In Unit 15 Lesson 1, students will graph and analyze their data as part of their study of patterns in math and science. This lesson can be integrated into a science class discussion about plants.

Key Content

- Measuring length in cm.
- Collecting data over time.
- Identifying the manipulated, responding, and fixed variables in an experiment.
- Connecting mathematics and science to real-world situations: measuring plant growth.

Key Vocabulary

fixed variable
manipulated variable
responding variable
scientific time

Daily Practice and Problems: Bits for Lesson 5

W. What Fraction? (URG p. 23)

1. $\frac{2}{3}$ of Mrs. Dewey's class went on a field trip.

   A. What fraction of the class did not go on the field trip?

   B. Did more or less than $\frac{1}{2}$ of the class go on the trip?

2. $\frac{3}{8}$ of Mrs. Randall's class went on the field trip.

   A. What fraction of the class did not go on the field trip?

   B. Did more or less than $\frac{1}{2}$ of the class go on the trip?

3. Mr. Henry's entire class went on the field trip. $\frac{5}{8}$ of Mr. Henry's class brought sandwiches for lunch. $\frac{2}{8}$ brought salads. The rest of the class brought fruit. What fraction of the class brought fruit?

Y. Order Fractions (URG p. 24)

1. Which is greater $\frac{1}{12}$ or $\frac{1}{10}$? How did you decide?

2. Which is greater $\frac{3}{5}$ or $\frac{3}{8}$? How did you decide?

3. Which is greater $1\frac{1}{2}$ or $\frac{5}{4}$? How did you decide?

DPP Task and Challenge are on page 82. Suggestions for using the DPPs are on page 82.

Materials List

	Math Facts and Daily Practice and Problems	Lab
Student Book — Student Guide		*Plant Growth* Pages 379–381
Teacher Resources — Unit Resource Guide	DPP Items W–Z Pages 23–25 ⊙	
Teacher Resources — Generic Section ⊙		*Three-column Data Table,* 1 per student

⊙ *available on Teacher Resource CD*

All Transparency Masters, Blackline Masters, and Assessment Blackline Masters in the Unit Resource Guide are on the Teacher Resource CD.

Supplies for Each Student or Student Pair

container for planting
four seeds (lima beans or sunflower seeds work well)
one cup of potting soil
paper towels
centimeter ruler
graduated cylinder
craft sticks marked at $\frac{1}{2}$ inch, optional

Materials for the Teacher

Transparency of *Three-column Data Table* (Unit Resource Guide, Generic Section), optional

Before the Lab

Students plant the seeds on the second day of this lesson and begin to collect plant height data as soon as a sprout breaks through the soil. Both lima bean seeds and sunflower seeds usually take 4 to 5 days to sprout; therefore, the seeds should be planted on a Thursday or Friday as there will be less chance that the sprouts will break through the soil over a weekend.

Each student can plant his or her own pot of seeds and collect data individually or students can work in pairs to plant the seeds and collect the data. Students need to collect their plant growth data over 21 days. There are not 21 days between this lesson and its conclusion in Unit 15 according to the suggested class sessions in the unit outlines. You may have to teach that lesson out of the order in which it falls in the curriculum.

Developing the Lab

Part 1. Introduction to Plant Growth

Read the Introduction to Plant Growth section of *Plant Growth* Lab Pages in the *Student Guide* together. In *Question 1A,* students are asked to identify the two variables: plant height, *H,* and time, *T.* Students are asked to consider the most appropriate unit of measurement for measuring plant height *(Question 1B).* Though you could use either standard units (inches) or metric units (centimeters), we recommend that you measure to the nearest half-centimeter. This will make the growth pattern easier to see when it has been graphed. In this experiment, time will be measured in days *(Question 1C).* This will allow students to see the small changes that occur in the plant's height as it grows. The manipulated variable is time, *T,* measured in days, since that is the variable for which we can choose the values *(Question 1D).* That is, we choose the days on which we measure the plants. The responding variable is plant height, *H,* measured in centimeters since we find the values of this variable as a result of doing the experiment *(Question 1E).*

In the second part of this vignette, Mrs. Dewey introduces her class to scientific time *(Question 2).* Scientific time always starts at $T = 0$. The use of scientific time provides us with a common time frame so that we can compare plant growth at different times of the year. For example, if you did this experiment in November and then again in April, you could compare the results since both experiments use a common time frame, each starting at $T = 0$ days. Each student or student pair will start their scientific clock when the first sprout breaks through the soil. This means that

Plant Growth

Introduction to Plant Growth

Discuss

The students in Mrs. Dewey's class are studying plants and how they grow. To help the students see how plants grow, Mrs. Dewey suggested that they design an experiment that can be done in their classroom.

"Why don't we each plant a seed and then measure how tall our plants grow each day?" suggested Grace.

"That's a great idea," echoed Jerome and Maya. "Then, we can graph our data and see if all of our plants have the same growth pattern."

"That would make a good experiment," said Mrs. Dewey.

I. A. What are the two main variables in this experiment?
   B. What unit of measurement should the students use to measure plant height? Explain your thinking.
   C. How should students measure time in this experiment: days, minutes, hours, etc.? Explain your thinking.
   D. Which variable is the manipulated variable?
   E. Which variable is the responding variable?

"During our experiment, we will use scientific time instead of calendar time," said Mrs. Dewey. "Scientific time always starts at $T = 0$. So, in our experiment, we will start at $T = 0$ days. You will each start your scientific clock when your plant first pushes out of the soil. Let's say that this happens on March 21. We would then call this date $T = 0$ days. March 22 would then be $T = 1$ day."

March

S	M	T	W	Th	F	Sa
			1	2	3	4	5
6	7	8	9	10	11	12
13	14	15	16	17	18	19
20	(21)	22	23	24	25	26
27	28	29	30	31		

Plant Growth   SG · Grade 4 · Unit 13 · Lesson 5   379

Student Guide - Page 379

2. How is scientific time different from calendar time?

"To keep our experiment fair, there are variables that will need to be held fixed," continued Mrs. Dewey.

3. A. What variables should be held fixed in this experiment?
   B. Why is it important to hold these variables fixed?

The students in Mrs. Dewey's class decided on the following setup for their experiment. Your class may need to use a different setup.

- Each student will plant four bean seeds in a clean $\frac{1}{2}$-pint milk carton saved from the lunchroom.
- Each student will plant their seeds $\frac{1}{2}$-inch deep.
- Each student will choose one of his or her plants to measure during the experiment, cutting off any other plants that grow.
- Students will measure their plants on Monday, Wednesday, and Friday mornings and will record their measurements on a data table.
- Plants will be watered with the same amount of water after they are measured on Mondays and Fridays.

380 SG · Grade 4 · Unit 13 · Lesson 5   **Plant Growth**

Student Guide - Page 380

different students or student pairs may begin their scientific clocks on different days. In **Question 2,** students compare scientific time to calendar time. Scientific time is different from calendar time because no matter what the date on the calendar is, the scientific clock starts at $T = 0$, in this case, $T = 0$ days.

For **Question 3,** students identify the variables that need to be held fixed in this experiment in order to make it fair. The variables that should be fixed are those variables that are kept constant for each experimental setup. The fixed variables in this experiment are summarized below:

Variables That Should Be Fixed	Recommendations
• number of seeds planted by each student	4 seeds per pot
• type of seeds planted	lima bean or sunflower seeds
• size of container used as a pot	school milk carton
• type of soil	potting soil
• amount of soil used in each pot	1 cup
• depth of each seed	$\frac{1}{2}$ inch
• amount of light each plant will receive	(see Part 2 for details)
• amount of water each plant will receive	(see Part 2 for details)
• time of day plant is measured	as part of morning routine

By controlling all these variables, you can collect a set of class data allowing you to compare how the various seeds grew.

In the final part of the vignette, the experimental setup that Mrs. Dewey's students will use is described. This is one way to do this experiment. In this setup, students each plant four lima bean seeds in a $\frac{1}{2}$-pint milk carton. A 9- or 12-ounce paper cup will also work as a pot. It is recommended that each student or student pair plant four seeds in a pot, increasing the probability that at least one plant will come up in each pot. Seeds should be planted at a depth of $\frac{1}{2}$ inch and should be spread out in the pot as much as possible. The plants should all be watered on the same days, and each plant will receive the same amount of water. The plants will be kept on a shelf next to the window so that each plant will receive the same amount of light.

Content Note

When using scientific time, we usually consider both the date an event occurs and the hour and even minute when the event occurs. For example, if a plant first breaks through the soil at 10:00 A.M. on March 3rd, this would be noted as $T = 0$. The plant should then be measured each day at exactly 10:00 A.M. For our purposes, we will not be concerned with the hour, considering only the date when the plant first breaks through the soil as $T = 0$.

Content Note

Despite your best efforts to control the variables, individual plants will probably not exhibit identical growth. It is very difficult to control all the variables in an experiment like this. In particular, one variable we cannot control in the classroom is the genetic makeup of each plant. However, the genetic variation in commercially produced seeds is usually very small. This is the reason that corn plants in a corn field are generally the same height.

TIMS Tip

Lima bean seeds have been recommended for this lab because they are easy for students to handle, they grow quickly, and the plants are fairly sturdy. You could also use sunflower seeds (not the roasted or sterile ones) to complete this lab. However, the plants are not as sturdy. Lima beans can be purchased at any grocery store. The sunflower seeds found in bird seed mixtures work well in this experiment. You may also want to experiment with other seeds.

Students should begin their measurements as soon as the first plant is visible above the soil. As the other plants begin to sprout, they should be cut at soil level so as not to disturb the plant you will be measuring. (*Note:* Before cutting the extra sprouts, see the Extension later in this Lesson Guide.) If these sprouts are not cut as they grow, they can become tangled with the plant you are measuring.

As the plants grow, students measure their plant height to the nearest half-centimeter three to four times each week. Students should measure from the soil to the base of the first set of leaves as shown in Figure 13.

After you have completed the discussion material in the *Student Guide,* students can draw a picture of their lab setup. Sample student work is shown in Figure 14. This picture can be completed as independent work while students plant their seeds in small groups during the second day of this lesson, or it can be assigned as homework between day 1 and day 2.

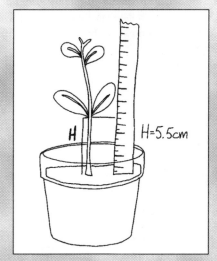

Figure 13: *Measuring plant growth*

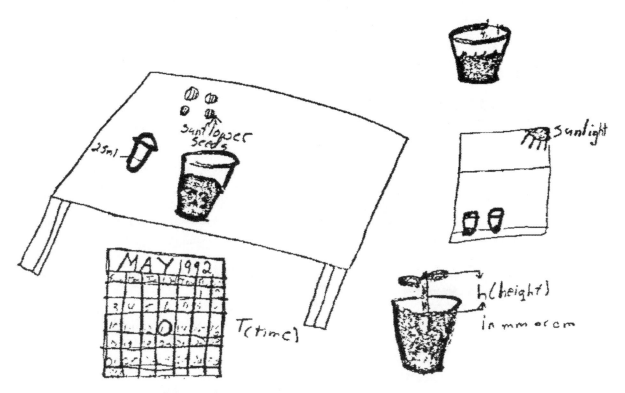

Figure 14: *A sample student picture for plant growth*

Draw

Your class will now complete a plant growth experiment like the one described by the students in Mrs. Dewey's class. Draw a picture of your experimental setup. Be sure to label the variables using symbols.

4. What variables will you measure in this experiment?

 Collect

Plant your seeds. As soon as the first sprout breaks through the soil, begin your scientific clock.

- Measure the height of your first sprout to the base of the first set of leaves several times each week.
- Measure to the nearest half centimeter.
- Use a data table similar to the one shown here to record your data.
- Continue to collect data over at least 21 days.

Plant Growth

Date	T in Days	H in cm
March 21	0	0 cm
March 23	2	1 cm
March 25	4	3 cm

You will graph and analyze your data from this experiment in Unit 15 Lesson 1.

Plant Growth   SG · Grade 4 · Unit 13 · Lesson 5 381

Student Guide - Page 381

Part 2. Planting Seeds

During the second day of this lesson, students will plant their seeds. This is an activity that is best completed with small groups of students, so you will need to plan work for students to complete independently or in small groups when they are not planting their seeds.

Have students come to the planting area in small groups or a few pairs at a time. Each student or student pair will need a container for their seeds. If you are using milk cartons from the lunchroom, make sure they have been washed out. Have students punch two to three small holes in the bottom of their containers for water drainage. They then put 1 cup of soil into their containers. Students should make four small holes in the soil each about $\frac{1}{2}$ inch deep. They then plant their four seeds, covering them carefully with soil. Once the seeds have been planted, students should water them carefully. Although the amount of water will depend on your soil or the climate conditions in your classroom, it is important to make sure that each student uses the same amount of water. Students can use a graduated cylinder to measure their water. The finished pots should be placed in trays where they will all be approximately the same distance from a window or lamp. Place a folded paper towel under each pot to catch excess water.

Once planting has been completed, students need to maintain their plants throughout the experiment. Plants should be watered several times a week. The amount of water plants receive will depend on the type of soil used; however, the important thing is that all plants should be watered on the same day and each plant should receive the same amount of water.

Once the plants have started to grow, they should be handled carefully when they are being measured. Students should measure their plants' height to the nearest half-centimeter several times each week. They should measure their plants at about the same time of day. Plants should be measured from the soil level to the base of the first set of leaves as was shown in Figure 13. Some plants tend to split or branch out near the top, making it difficult to find the top of the plant. Measuring to the base of the first set of leaves will provide us with a discrete part of the plant to measure. Because of the way plants grow, the data you collect by measuring to the base of the first leaf provides a general index as to the way the plant would grow in its natural environment. A second reason to measure in this way is that the seeds will continue to grow throughout the 21 days; that is, they will not use up the nutrients available to them in the soil within that time. This means that the plants' growth may not level off and you will not see the growth curve, as shown in Figure 15. Note, this graph shows that the plant's growth, as measured to the base of the first set of leaves, began to level off after $T = 18$ days. Students will plot and explore their plant growth data in a graph in Unit 15.

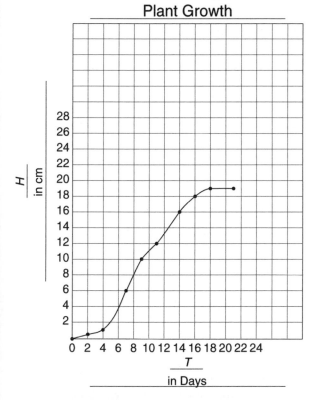

Figure 15: *A sample graph showing the growth curve of a plant*

Students should record their plant height data on a *Three-column Data Table*. A sample student data table is shown in Figure 16.

Note that this plant first sprouted on October 19. This date starts that scientific clock and is labeled at $T = 0$ days. Since the plant was just visible above the soil, the measurement was 0 centimeters. The next time the plant was measured was on October 21. This was two days after the plant sprouted and is therefore labeled $T = 2$ days.

Content Note

Plants tend to grow continuously throughout their lives. Primary growth takes place at the tip of each stem and root, where cells are actively dividing. These cells then elongate, which accounts for most of the increase in length of stems and roots. Secondary growth is that which adds girth to a plant, such as trees. Trees exhibit both primary and secondary growth. Herbaceous (nonwoody) plants, such as lima beans and sunflowers, generally exhibit only primary growth.

Plant Growth

Date	T in Days	H in cm
10-19	0	0
10-21	2	$\frac{1}{2}$
10-23	4	1
10-26	7	6
10-28	9	10
10-30	11	12
11-2	14	16
11-4	16	18
11-6	18	19
11-9	21	19

Figure 16: *A sample student data table*

Daily Practice and Problems:
Task & Challenge for Lesson 5

X. Task: Money (URG p. 24)

1. What is the least number of coins (quarters, dimes, or nickels) needed to make $1.20?

2. What is the greatest number of quarters, dimes, or nickels needed to make 85 cents?

Z. Challenge: Favorite Sports
(URG p. 25)

Mrs. Dewey conducted a survey to find out the favorite sports of the students in her class. John, Nicholas, and Ana each voted for a different sport — soccer, hockey, or baseball. Each of these three sports received either 9, 6, or 5 votes. Use the clues below to find out who voted for which sport and the number of votes each sport received.

Clue 1: John's sport received more votes than hockey.

Clue 2: Hockey is the favorite sport of the girl.

Clue 3: John's sport received fewer votes than baseball.

Suggestions for Teaching the Lesson

Homework and Practice

- Assign the picture of the experimental setup as homework between the first and the second day of this lesson.

- DPP Bits W and Y review fractions. Task X provides practice with money.

Assessment

Use the picture of the lab setup as assessment. Check to see if students identified the two main variables of the experiment as well as the fixed variables. See Figure 14 for an example of a good picture.

Extension

- Make a class frequency distribution showing the number of seeds that sprouted in a cup. For example, if you have 30 students in your classroom and each student planted four seeds, ask how many cups had no seeds sprout, how many had one seed sprout, how many had two seeds sprout, how many had three, and how many had four. Make a class data table and graph similar to those shown in Figure 17.

  Use your class data to find the probability that a seed will sprout. For example, if you have 30 cups with four seeds in each cup, it is possible that 120 seeds could sprout. To find the probability that a seed will sprout, count the number of actual sprouts that came up in your class. If 90 plants out of 120 plants sprouted, the probability that any one seed would sprout is $\frac{90}{120}$ or $\frac{3}{4}$.

- DPP Challenge Z is a logic puzzle.

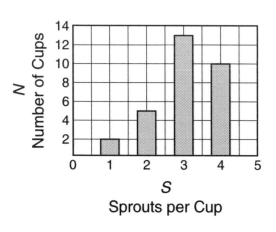

S Sprouts per Cup	N Number of Cups
0	0
1	2
2	5
3	13
4	10

Figure 17: *A sample frequency distribution*

AT A GLANCE

Math Facts and Daily Practice and Problems

DPP Bits W and Y review fractions. Task X and Challenge Z require problem-solving skills.

Part 1. Introduction to Plant Growth

1. Read the vignette on the *Plant Growth* Activity Pages in the *Student Guide.*
2. Answer *Questions 1–3* in class.
3. Review the experimental setup following *Question 3.*
4. Students draw a picture of the experimental setup that will be used in your class.

Part 2. Planting Seeds

1. Students plant their seeds.
2. Students collect plant height data starting on the day the plant first breaks through the soil.
3. Students measure their plant's height from the soil to the base of the first set of leaves, to the nearest half centimeter, two to three times each week for at least three weeks.
4. Students record their plant height data on a *Three-column Data Table*. This lab will be completed in Unit 15 Lesson 1.

Homework

Students can draw their pictures for homework.

Assessment

Use students' drawings of the lab setup as an assessment.

Notes:

Student Guide

Questions 1–4 (SG pp. 379–381)

1. **A.** *Plant Height *(H)* and Time *(T)*
   B. *centimeters
   C. *Days. The plant height is measured each day.
   D. *Time in days, T
   E. *Plant Height, H

2. No matter what the date on the calendar is, scientific time starts with $T = 0$.

3. **A.** *Number of seeds in a pot, type of seeds, size of container, type of soil, amount of soil, depth of seeds, amount of light, amount of water, time of day plant is measured.
   B. In order to study plant growth over time, variables such as the amount of water and sunlight must be held fixed so that we know that the changes in the rate of growth are not due to these variables.

4. Plant height, time, amount of water, depth of soil

---

*Answers and/or discussion are included in the Lesson Guide.

**Answers for all the Home Practice in the *Discovery Assignment Book* are at the end of the unit.

Discovery Assignment Book

Part 2. Working with Remainders

Questions 1–4 (DAB p. 213)

Explanations will vary.

1. 4 crates; $30 \div 9 = 3$ crates R3 boxes. The remainder tells us that one more crate is needed to ship all the boxes.

2. 9 children

3. No, the correct answer should be $90 \times 3 = \$270$. $\$273 - \$270 = \$3$; Mrs. Roberts collected $3.00 too much.

4. About 50 pages. Students can round 453 to 450. $450 \div 9 = 50$ pages.

Part 3. Multiplication and Division Practice

Questions 1–2 (DAB p. 214)

1. **A.** 1869
   B. 1794
   C. 1740
   D. 29,200
   E. 48,032
   F. 89 R2
   G. 189 R1
   H. 58 R3

2. Possible strategy: Skip count by 250 seven times – 250, 500, 750, 1000, 1250, 1500, 1750.

Part 4. More Division Practice

Questions A–D (DAB p. 214)

A. 601
B. 655 R2
C. 1335
D. 95

Part 5. Create a Fraction

Questions A–D (DAB p. 215)

A. $\frac{2}{3}$
B. $\frac{1}{10}$
C. $\frac{1}{5}$ or $\frac{2}{10}$
D. $\frac{10}{12}$

Part 6. Prizes

Questions 1–4 (DAB p. 215)

1. Answers will vary. Possible solution: 16 large, 8 medium, 40 tiny stuffed animals

2. Answers will vary.

3. $16 \times \$5 + 8 \times \$2 + 40 \times \$.10 = \$100$

4. Another possible solution: 15 large, 10 medium, 50 tiny stuffed animals

Part 7. Solving Problems

Questions 1–5 (DAB p. 216)

1. **A.** 145 minutes
   B. About $2\frac{1}{2}$ hrs or between 2 and 3 hrs

2. 45 minutes

3. 35 minutes

4. **A.** more than; 50 hrs $= 50 \times 60$ min $= 3000$ min
   B. less than; 100 hrs $= 100 \times 60$ min $= 6000$ min
   C. Answers will vary. Possible solution: $5400 \div 60 = 90$ hrs

5. **A.** less; 1650 minutes less
   B. 27.5 hours

*Answers and/or discussion are included in the Lesson Guide.